The design of hydraulic
components and systems

The design of hydraulic components and systems

Hugh Martin
University of Waterloo

ELLIS HORWOOD
LONDON NEW YORK TORONTO SYDNEY TOKYO SINGAPORE
MADRID MEXICO CITY MUNICH

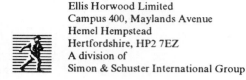

First published 1995 by
Ellis Horwood Limited
Campus 400, Maylands Avenue
Hemel Hempstead
Hertfordshire, HP2 7EZ
A division of
Simon & Schuster International Group

Printed and bound in Great Britain by
Redwood Books, Trowbridge, Wiltshire

Library of Congress Cataloging-in-Publication Data

Martin, Hugh.
        The design of hydraulic components and systems / Hugh Martin.
            p.   cm.
        Includes bibliographical references and index.
        ISBN 0-13-297194-1 (pbk.)
        1. Fluid power technology.   2. Hydraulic machinery – Design and
construction.   I. Title.
        TJ843.M34   1995
        620.1'06 – dc20   94-41388
                                                                            CIP

British Library Cataloguing in Publication Data

A catalogue record for this book is available
from the British Library

ISBN 0-13-297194-1

---

1 2 3 4 5   99 98 97 96 95

*This book is dedicated to
my three grandsons*

Andrew, Cameron and Eric

Contents

4. Leakage, friction and filters

5. Valve design and application

6. Hydraulic pumps and motors

Preface

Students of engineering will, most likely, come into contact with fluid power components or systems at some time in their career. A wide range of industries, for example, transportation, aerospace, agriculture, robotics and machine tools to name a few, all use fluid power components to one degree or another. Many manufacturing processes, especially where automation plays a major role use systems that are either pneumatic or hydraulic in their construction. More recently, the major impact of microprocessor technology has touched the fluid power industry, resulting in the development of digitally controlled electrohydraulic systems, controlled either by computer or programmable logic controllers. However, these topics are beyond the level of this text.

In spite of the industries increasing use of fluid power, fully trained engineers in this important field are still scarce. The topic is still not a core subject in most university and college programs. This has resulted in many hydraulic and pneumatic component suppliers undertaking the education of their own and their customers staff.

The objective of the book is to provide a teaching text in this important engineering topic. It ties together basic engineering science topics, such as fluid mechanics, thermodynamics control theory and dynamics, with system design. It hopes to explain to the engineering student how to assess the performance of, evaluate the design of, or trouble shoot, fluid power components and circuits. The topics are extensively illustrated with meaningful worked examples, and there are also tutorial problems for student practice. Engineers in industry may also find the book useful as a reference.

The purpose of the text is to fill the gap between the maintenance/repair type book, used in technician courses, and the advanced fluid power control systems texts used as resource material by graduate students and other researchers.

There are eight chapters in the book, which can be summarized as follows:

Chapter 1 provides a review of the basic background material needed in the design of fluid power circuits and components.

Chapter 2 discusses dynamic behaviour in general terms. This is introduced because fluid power circuits are subjected to more than the steady flow condition taught in fluid mechanics courses. It is often useful to develop a conceptual model using block diagrams and borrow from control system theory, together with its methods of analysis. Dynamic response is a very important part of any fluid power design.

Chapter 3 uses the general ideas of Chapter 2 and applies them to fluid power systems to assess component stiffness, natural frequencies and the dynamic response of rams. Failure of a circuit to perform to specification can often be traced to inadequate attention being given to the dynamic aspects of the design.

Chapter 4, in the main, deals with those aspects that contribute to energy wastage and potential pollution problems. Leakage can cause oil spills, as can seal failure. On the other hand, seals can create excessive friction, which in turn can use more energy than necessary. Poor filtration can cause maintenance problems or even failure. On the other hand, analysis of filtered particles can give information about excessive wear in the circuit.

Chapter 5 deals in some detail with what is probably that most important component in a system, and often the most troublesome, the valve. The performance of this component is non-linear, since its output flow is a function of two variables. A linearization approach is developed for both the valve and the valve connected to a ram.

Chapter 6 discusses the performance of pumps and motors. Also included is the hydrostatic transmission, since it is so widely used in industry.

Chapter 7 deals with an often neglected component, the accumulator. This is a multi-function device that has come to the forefront due to the emphasis on energy conservation.

Chapter 8 ties together all the components discussed in the previous section, and develops the basic ideas for system design.

Grateful acknowledgement is made to the students who have helped to develop the course material, on which this book is based, over many years at the University of Waterloo. Thanks is also offered to my colleagues, Dr Ken Adams, who co-teaches the course, Professor D. McCloy, who co-authored the companion book for advanced students, Dr Jean Thoma, for the many useful discussions we have had over the years, Professor Emeritus Sandy Freidman, for his help and contributions to the topic, and Kathy Roenspiess for her excellent typing and editing of the original class notes for the course. Many of the examples used may have originated from other sources too numerous to remember over the years, so I would like to acknowledge the contributions to all these contributors to fluid power technology.

Finally I would like to offer my thanks to my wife Pat for proofreading the text and for her continued long-suffering support over several book preparation projects.

Dept of Mechanical Engineering   Hugh R Martin
University of Waterloo
Waterloo, Ontario
Canada
February 1995

Nomenclature

A, a	Area	(m^2)
	Damping coefficient	(N.s/m)
	Width	(m)
C	Compressibility	(m^2/N)
	A constant	
C_d	Discharge coefficient	
C_h	Fluid capacitance	$(\text{m}^4.\text{s}^2/\text{kg})$
C_m	Pneumatic flow coefficient	
C_p	Specific heat at constant pressure	(J/kg.K)
C_v	Specific heat at constant volume	(J/kg.K)
C_{pg}	Pressure gain	$(\text{m}^3/\text{s/Pa})$
C_{xv}	Flow gain	$(\text{m}^3/\text{s/m})$
C_d^p	Pump drag coefficient	(N.m/rpm)
C_l^p	Pump slip flow coefficient	$(\text{m}^3/\text{s/Pa})$
D_p	Pump displacement	(m^3/rev)
D_m	Motor displacement	(m^3/rev)
d	Diameter	(m)
d_h	Hydraulic diameter	(m)
d/dt	Derivative with respect to time	$(1/\text{s})$
E	Young's modulus, Energy	$(\text{N/m}^2; \text{J})$
e	Eccentricity	(m)
	Effort variable	
F	Force	(N)
f	Pipe friction coefficient, Flow variable	
f_n	Natural frequency	(Hz)
G	Modulus of rigidity, Conductance	$(\text{N/m}^2; \text{m}^3/\text{s/Pa})$
g	Acceleration due to gravity	(m/s^2)
H	Head	(m)
h	Separation distance	(m)
	Height	(m)
	Heat transfer coefficient	$(\text{watts/m}^2.\text{K})$

I	Moment of inertia	(kg.m^2)
I_h	Fluid inertance	(kg/m^4)
J	Polar moment of inertia of section	(m^4)
j	Complex number	
k	Spring rate	(N/m)
l	Length	(m)
M,m	Mass	(kg)
N	Bulk modulus, Shaft speed	(Pa; rpm)
n	Number of pistons, Integer	
p	Pressure	(Pa)
Q	Flow	(m^3/s)
Q	Amount of heat	(Joules)
q	Heat flow	(W, J/s)
R	Gas constant	(J/kg.K)
R'	Universal gas constant	(J/kg.K)
r	Radius	(m)
Re	Reynolds number	
R_h	Fluid resistance (laminar flow)	(kg/m^4.s)
s	Laplace variable	
T	Temperature	(°C; K)
	Torque	(N.m)
	Time constant	(s)
t	Time	(s)
	Wall thickness	(m)
V	Volume	(m^3)
v	Velocity	(m/s)
W	Mass flow	(kg/s)
	Power	(watts)
w	Gear width	(m)
x	Distance	(m)
	Input signal	
y	Oil film thickness	(m)
	Output signal	
Z	Elevation	(m)
	Impedance	
α	Swash plate angle	(deg)
	Angular acceleration	(rad/s)
	Root of equation	
γ	Ratio of specific heats	
ϵ	Error	
ζ	Damping ratio	
η_p^m	Mechanical efficiency of a pump	

η_p^v	Volumetric efficiency of a pump	
θ	Shaft angle	(deg)
	Phase shift	(deg)
λ	Oil spring stiffness	(N/m)
μ	Dynamic viscosity	(Pa.s)
	Dry friction coefficient	
ν	Kinematic viscosity	(m^2/s)
ρ	Density	(kg/m^3)
σ	Thermal conductivity	(watts/m.K)
τ	Shear stress	(Pa)
ω	Angular velocity	(rads/s)
	Angular frequency	(rads/s)
ω_n	Natural frequency	(rads/s)

Conversions

Length (m)

in	2.540×10^{-2}
ft	0.3048
cm	10^{-2}
m	10^{-3}

Area (m²)

in²	6.452×10^{-4}
ft²	9.290×10^{-2}
cm²	10^{-4}
mm²	10^{-6}

Volume (m³)

in	1.639×10^{-5}
ft³	2.832×10^{-2}
gal(UK)	4.546×10^{-3}
gal(US)	3.785×10^{-3}
cm³	10^{-6}
mm³	10^{-9}
litre	10^{-3}
ml(cc)	10^{-6}

Mass (kg)

lb	0.4536
Slug	14.606
Ton(UK)	1.016×10^{3}

Flow (Volume m³/s)

ft³/s	2.832×10^{-2}
ft³/min	4.719×10^{-4}
gpm(UK)	7.567×10^{-5}
gpm(US)	6.308×10^{-3}
litre/s	1×10^{-3}

Flow (Mass kg/s)

lb/s	0.4536
lb/hr	1.260×10^{-4}

Density (kg/m³)

lb/in³	2.768×10^{4}
lb/ft³	16.108
slug/ft³	5.154×10^{2}
g/cm³	1×10^{3}

Force (N, kg.s²/m)

lbf	4.448
Dyne	1×10^{-5}

Moment of Inertia

lb.m²	2.926×10^{-4}
lb.ft²	4.214×10^{-2}
Slug.ft²	1.356

Ton(US)	0.907×10^3
tonne	10^3

Pressure (Pa N/m^2)

in(water)	2.491×10^2
in(mercury)	3.386×10^2
lb.in^2	6.895×10^3
bar	10^5
mbar	10^2
Atmosphere	101.325×10^3
dyne/cm	10^{-1}
torr	1.333×10^2

Power, Heat Flow (W, J/s)

ft.lbf/s	1.356
HP	745.7
BTU/hr	0.293
kcal/hr	1.163

Energy, Work, Torque

(J, N.m, W.s)

ft.lbf	1.356
BTU	1.055×10^3
Cal	4.187
Erg	1.00×10^{-7}
Dyne.cm	1.00×10^{-7}

Viscosity (Dynamic, Pa.s)

cP(oise)	1×10^{-3}
lb/ft.s	1.488
cS(okes)	1.00×10^{-6}
ft^2/s	9.29×10^{-2}
cm^2/s	1.00×10^{-4}

Specific Heat (J/m^3.K)
(Constant Volume)

BTU/ft^3.°F 6.707×10^4

Specific Heat (J/kg.K)
(Constant Pressure)

BTU/lb.°F 4.187×10^3

Thermal Conductivity
(J/m.s.K)

BTU/ft.hr.°F   1.731

Heat Transfer
(J/m^2.s.K)

Btu/ft^2.hr.°F   5.678

Temperature

$$°C = (°F - 32)/1.8$$
$$K = °C + 273.15$$
$$°R = °F + 460$$

Typical values

	Density	Bulk Mod.	c	μ	υ
	kg/m^3	Pa	m/s	Pa.s	m^2/s
Oil	858.2	1.38×10^9	1268	3.4×10^{-2}	4.0×10^{-5}
Water	1000.0	2.18×10^9	1478	1.5×10^{-3}	1.5×10^{-6}
Air	1.187	αP	343	1.8×10^{-5}	1.5×10^{-5}

Fluid compressibility can also be estimated as 1% by volume for every 13.78 MPa of applied pressure.

CHAPTER 1

Background to fluid power

1.1 Introduction

The movement and control of fluids under pressure have played a major role in virtually every area of engineering. The flow of fluid, with the objective of delivering a quantity of liquid from a source to a destination, comes under the heading of transportation. An example of this would be filling a vehicle's tank with petrol; the fluid is simply transported from the fuel pump to the tank. Fluid power, on the other hand, has the objective of using the fluid under pressure to perform some form of work.

The term fluids, can refer to either liquids or gases, and fluid power is the general term used for hydraulics and pneumatics. The main difference between the two media is that hydraulic oil provides a very stiff medium for transmitting power and can thus provide large forces to move loads with a high level of accuracy. On the other hand, air, while less expensive and more environmentally friendly, provides a much softer system.

Water has been used as a means of transmitting power from before the second century B.C. For example [1], Ctesibius, who was born in Alexandria, has been credited with inventing the first positive displacement pump. Its purpose was to produce a jet of water for fighting fires. He also designed a type of organ, in which water pressure was used to produce air flow and hence sound. It is thought that the word hydraulic was first introduced to describe this instrument. Another well-known pump in botany is the way sap is pumped up trees every spring. The pressure developed in a 15 m vine for example, is about fourteen times that produced by the human heart. Nature does not pump in the usual sense of the word, but draws the sap up by surface tension.

Early fluid power devices moved large volumes of fluid at relatively low pressures. The product of pressure and flow is power, and the aim of the designer over the years has been to increase pressure greatly, so that the power can be packaged more efficiently. The higher the pressure, the smaller the flow to produce the required power. Until around 1920, these devices were limited due

1

to the lack of suitable seals, then a major breakthrough came with the discovery of synthetic rubber, which allowed the industry to make significant advances in design.

The application of fluid power, both oil and gas, has touched every area of engineering. Examples include machine tools, earth-moving equipment, steel manufacture, medical engineering, aerospace, marine and many other areas too numerous to mention.

1.2 Comparisons between power handling methods

Devices that are used to handle fluid power lie somewhere between electrical and mechanical power transmission devices. Fluid and electrical systems transmit power more easily over appreciable distances than their mechanical equivalents. Electrical devices are especially good in this respect at low power levels. The introduction of the microprocessor and small-chip technology has made the combination of electro-fluid systems a very attractive feature for most manufacturing applications.

Table 1.1 is an attempt to summarize the salient features of the various system approaches. The choice the designer may finally make will be greatly influenced by the specification requirements and operating environment.

Table 1.1

Characteristic	Rating		
	1	2	3
Torque / Inertia Load	H	P	M, EM
Power Out / Weight	H, P	—	EM*, M
Steady-State Stiffness	H	M	P, EM
Level of Friction	EM	H, M	P
Speed of Response	—	H	P, EM
Sensitivity to Debris	EM, M	—	H+, P

Key: M — Mechanical   P — Pneumatic   * Worsens as power increases
      EM — Electromagnetic   H — Hydraulic   + Fluid filtration essential

A major advantage of fluid over electromagnetic power is that the former is not so limited by the physical properties of the materials used. For example, the saturation limit of steel used for magnets provides an equivalent pressure of around 1.7 MPa, so to provide more torque, an electric motor has to be bigger. On the other hand, the pressure applied to a hydraulic motor can be twenty or more times greater without increasing the motor size.

1.3 The basics

Fluid power system design gathers together the fundamentals of fluid mechanics, thermodynamics, vibration analysis, applied mechanics and systems engineering. It is truly an interdisciplinary topic area. It also requires some art, in that the actual components do not always exhibit well-behaved linear characteristics, and hence experience is a significant ingredient in the design of equipment. It is convenient at this stage to review the basics of the various disciplines listed above, so that the appropriate tools are readily available in this text, for reference.

1.3.1 Density, mass and force

Density is that property of a fluid or solid which is defined as the mass of matter in a unit volume of the substance. For liquids and solids, under normal conditions, it is assumed to be constant with respect to pressure and temperature variations. The symbol ρ (rho) is normally used to signify this property. If we consider Newton's Law of Motion,

$$F = m\,\frac{dv}{dt} \tag{1.1}$$

and from the definition given,

$$m = \rho\,V \tag{1.2}$$

then,

$$F = \rho\,V\frac{dv}{dt} \tag{1.3}$$

If the acceleration happens to be the acceleration due to gravity (g), then the force is called the weight of the object,

$$F = \rho V g \qquad (1.4)$$

If the substance is a fluid, then (1.3) can also be written as,

$$F = \rho Q v \qquad (1.5)$$

When a liquid is poured into a container, it forms a free surface if the container is not completely filled. A gas, on the other hand, behaves quite differently, as it will always expand to occupy the entire vessel. Gases are influenced by the pressure which is applied to them in a container. As pressure is increased, the volume of gas reduces. In fact it is also affected by temperature.

The change of density of a gas with temperature or pressure is governed by the Perfect Gas Law, to be discussed further in Section 1.4.

$$pV = mRT \qquad (1.6)$$

where p is the absolute pressure, and the temperature is recorded in Kelvin.
Hence, from (1.6),

$$\rho = \frac{m}{V} = \frac{p}{RT} \qquad (1.7)$$

The gas constant R for any gas can be obtained from the universal gas constant, R', divided by the molecular weight of that particular gas, see Table 1.2.

Some typical values for density are shown in Table 1.3. These values compare fire-resistant fluids with industrial hydraulic oil and air, in other words the normal fluids used in industry.

In dealing with gases, it is also important to differentiate between absolute and gauge pressures. Pressure is simply force per unit area, and the value measured by a pressure gauge or transducer is termed gauge pressure, since it does not include the fluctuations of air pressure due to the atmosphere.

There are some changes in density with temperature and pressure, as shown for a typical industrial oil in Table 1.4, but these are not considered to be significant and are usually ignored.

At sea level, the standard atmospheric pressure of 101.3 kPa(a) is developed due to the weight of the air above the earth's surface. The actual figure varies from day to day due to variations in weather conditions, and the height of the equipment above sea level. However, for most fluid power application, these

Table 1.2

Gas	Molecular Weight	R(J/kg.K)
Air	28.97	287.00
Nitrogen	28.02	296.76
Oxygen	32.00	259.84
Hydrogen	2.02	4124.50

Universal gas constant $R' = 8315$ J/kg.K

Table 1.3

	FRF	Water in Oil	Mineral Oil	Air (38°C)
Density(kg/m^3)	1136.0	980.0	858.2	1.187

Table 1.4

Temperature (°C)	Density (kg/m^3) at Pressures Quoted		
	101.3 kPa	17.24 MPa	34.47 MPa
20	870.0	878.8	887.6
30	862.7	871.8	882.2
40	856.7	866.7	876.7
50	851.0	861.0	871.0
60	842.2	853.8	865.5
70	837.2	848.9	860.0
80	832.2	843.3	854.4

variations are too small to be of any significance to the designer,

$$\text{Gauge Pressure} = \text{Absolute Pressure} - 101.3$$

The term vacuum is usually applied to any gas pressure value which is less than 101.3 kPa.

1.3.2 Viscosity

Viscosity is a measure of a fluid's resistance to flow. It is probably the most important of all fluid properties, in that it wastes energy. A low-viscosity fluid flows easily, while a high viscosity is indicated by sluggish movement of a fluid. If we think of a viscous fluid in a pipe as a series of concentric thin- walled cylinders free to slide over each other like a telescope, then the fastest motion will be at the centre cylinder and the outer cylinder will be essentially stuck to the pipe wall. Hence, since one cylinder moves faster than the next, there will be frictional resistance between them, or one cylinder shears the next, giving rise to shear stresses in the fluid, as shown in Figure 1.1.

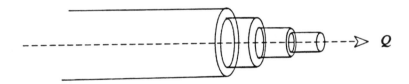

Figure 1.1 Viscous Flow Visualization

Hence, the dynamic viscosity μ (mu) is defined as,

$$\mu = \frac{\text{Shear Stress}}{\text{Shear Rate}} = \tau / \frac{dv}{dy} \qquad (1.8)$$

When the dynamic viscosity is divided by the fluid density, a new quantity results termed kinematic viscosity v (nu),

$$v = \frac{\mu}{\rho} \qquad (1.9)$$

Typical values for various fluids are shown in Table 1.5.

Table 1.5

	FRF	Water in Oil	Mineral Oil	Air (15.5°C, 101 kPa)
Viscosity(v) m^2/s	4.6×10^{-6}	0.15×10^{-5}	4.0×10^{-5}	1.5×10^{-5}

Rate of change of viscosity with temperature is expressed using an empirical number called the viscosity index (VI). A low index indicates a relatively large change with temperature, and vice versa. Hence hydraulic equipment used in the outdoors would benefit from oils with high index values [2]. The performance of a typical industrial hydraulic oil with respect to temperature and pressure is shown in Table 1.6.

Table 1.6

Temperature (°C)	Viscosity (x 10^{-6} m^2/s) at Pressures Quoted		
	101.3 kPa	17.24 MPa	34.47 MPa
10	150.0	225.0	300.0
20	85.0	126.9	168.8
30	47.5	70.6	95.8
40	30.0	43.6	57.0
50	21.1	29.7	38.3
60	14.6	21.1	27.7
70	10.9	15.1	19.3
80	8.0	11.1	14.1
90	6.5	8.7	10.9

When fluid is in motion it can exhibit two types of flow patterns, as observed by Osborne Reynolds in 1883 [3]. He showed that, depending on the relative magnitude of the variables involved, the flow can be smooth, like water from a tap nearly turned off, or irregular, like a tap turned fully on. The flow conditions are governed by the ratio of inertia to viscous forces in the flow,

$$Re = \frac{v d_h \rho}{\mu} = \frac{v d_h}{v} \propto \frac{\text{Inertia Forces}}{\text{Viscous Forces}} \qquad (1.10)$$

The transition from laminar to turbulent flow in pipes normally takes place when the Reynolds number increases through the range 1200 to 2500. Hence any value below 1200 is considered to indicate laminar flow, and above 2500 indicates turbulent flow. Normally for design purposes a figure of 2000 can be used.

The dimension, d_h, used in (1.10) is more generally called a characteristic length or hydraulic diameter, and is defined as,

$$d_h = \frac{4 \times \text{Flow Section Area}}{\text{Flow Section Perimeter}}$$

This is used in cases where the flow passage has a cross-sectional shape that is not circular, for example, a square section. For pipes, d_h is just the internal pipe diameter.

EXAMPLE 1.1

Oil flows at 1.6 l/s through a triangular section passage of side 15.0 mm. Determine the Reynolds number if the oil viscosity is 35 cSt. What condition is the flow experiencing? Should the pipe diameter be changed?

First we need to calculate the hydraulic diameter for a triangular section. If the side length is s, then

$$\text{Cross Sectional Area} = \frac{s\sqrt{s^2 - (s/2)^2}}{2} = s^2 \frac{\sqrt{3}}{4} = 9.743 \times 10^{-5} \text{m}^2$$

$$\text{Perimeter} = 3s = 0.045 \text{ m}$$

$$d_h = \frac{s\sqrt{s}}{3} = 0.008\ 66 \text{ m}$$

Now calculate the Reynolds number,

$$Re = \frac{vd_h}{v} = \frac{1.6 \times 10^{-3} \times 0.008\ 66}{9.743 \times 10^{-5} \times 35 \times 10^{-6}} = 4063.3$$

The flow is turbulent, causing excessive pressure drop and creating more noise than necessary. The cross-sectional area should be increased.

For the designer, viscosity results in pressure loss through pipes and components, which in turn means power wastage and fluid temperature increase. Turbulent flow also contributes to increased pressure loss, and creates noise.

1.3.3 Flow and pressure

Although Leonardo da Vinci (1452–1519) observed and sketched liquid jet behaviour, it was Evangelista Torricelli (1608–1647) who introduced the theorem stating that the velocity of a free jet of fluid is proportional to the square root of the head producing the jet. It was not until a century later that the constant of proportionality, $2g$, was introduced into the relationship. The simple demonstration of this theorem is shown in Figure 1.2, and introduces the idea of the orifice.

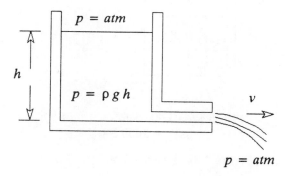

Figure 1.2 Torricelli's Theorem

Actually the theorem is essentially a special case of Bernoulli's equation, which will be discussed later in this section,

$$v = \sqrt{2gh} \qquad (1.11)$$

The term Head is sometimes used, especially with respect to pumps, or low-pressure pneumatics. It is measured in metres or a subset of that unit,

$$h = \frac{p}{g\rho} \qquad (1.12)$$

Around 1650, Blaise Pascal (1623-1662), laid down the principles of how fluids transmit power. The law states that the pressure in a fluid at rest is transmitted equally in all directions, so for example in Figure 1.3a, the pressure on each square metre of inside surface is 2000 Pa. A simple redesign of this device as shown in Figure 1.3b, with the piston area five times greater, results in a force at the piston rod of 500 N. This shows the force magnification effect of this law, and is the equivalent of the mechanical lever.

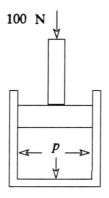

Piston area = 0.05 m²
p = 100/0.05 = 2000 Pa

Figure 1.3a Pascal's Law

One hundred years later, Daniel Bernoulli (1700-1782) introduced the concept of conservation of energy. Its application allows the designer to size pumps, valves and piping for efficient system operation. Bernoulli's equation is derived for this application, by applying the conservation of energy to a pipe of varying section and slope, as shown in Figure 1.4. A pump is used to force fluid into the pipe, and

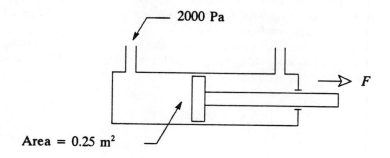

Figure 1.3b Application of Pascal's Law – The Ram

the fluid emerging is used to operate a fluid motor.

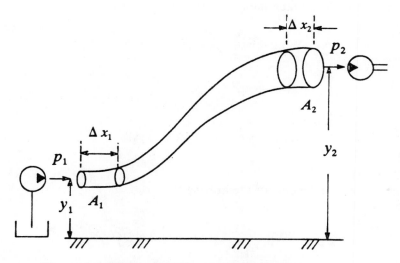

Figure 1.4 Bernoulli's Conservation of Energy

The conservation of energy simply states that energy can neither be created or destroyed, only converted from one form to another. This means that the total energy, in this case the potential energy due to elevation of the pipe, and the pressure, together with the kinetic energy due to fluid velocity, at any location must remain constant.

Consider an incompressible, non-viscous, fluid being pumped through the pipe, which has a varying cross-section. The pump is situated at an elevation of y_1, and the motor is at an elevation y_2, both above a reference ground level. The flow is considered as under steady conditions.

At the input to the pipe, the applied force is the pump delivery pressure, p_1, times the pipe cross-sectional area, A_1. Consider a volume of fluid pushed a distance Δx_1, into the pipe, such that,

$$\Delta V_1 = A_1 \Delta x_1$$

There will be a similiar volume at the exit of the pipe,

$$\Delta V_1 = A_2 \Delta x_2$$

and the volumes must be equal.

The work done at the pipe inlet is,

$$\text{Work done} = p_1 A_1 \Delta x_1 = p_1 \Delta V$$

and at the outlet,

$$\text{Work done} = p_2 A_2 \Delta x_2 = p_2 \Delta V$$

The change in kinetic energy of the moving fluid is,

$$\Delta KE = \frac{1}{2} \Delta m_2 v_2^2 - \frac{1}{2} \Delta m_1 v_1^2$$

where the elemental mass of fluid in each case is given by,

$$\Delta m_1 = \Delta x_1 A_1 \rho$$
$$\Delta m_2 = \Delta x_2 A_2 \rho$$

and since the volumes and densities are equal,

$$\Delta m_1 = \Delta m_2 = \Delta m$$

The change in potential energy of the fluid is dependent on the height of the pipe above the reference ground,

$$\Delta PE = \Delta m_2 g y_2 - \Delta m_1 g y_1$$

Now the conservation of energy stated that the total energy must be constant, hence,

$$p_1 \Delta V = \Delta KE + \Delta PE + \text{Work done by the motor}$$

$$= \Delta m \frac{(v_2^2 - v_1^2)}{2} + \Delta mg (y_2 - y_1) + p_2 \Delta V$$

$$(1.13)$$

but $\Delta m / \Delta V = \rho$, the fluid density, so equation (1.13) can be written,

$$p_1 + \frac{1}{2} \rho v_1^2 + g \rho y_1 = p_2 + \frac{1}{2} \rho v_2^2 + g \rho y_2$$

If the fluid is incompressible but viscous, then the friction of the fluid rubbing against the pipe walls causes energy to be dissipated as heat throughout the pipe. A temperature rise will occur and therefore some of the energy will not be available to do work. Hence, an additional term is added to the right-hand side of equation (1.13). If this equation is now divided by Δt, the power balance is found,

$$p_1 \frac{\Delta V}{\Delta t} = \frac{1}{2} \rho \frac{\Delta V}{\Delta t} (v_2^2 - v_1^2) + \frac{\Delta V}{\Delta t} \rho g (y_2 - y_1) + p_2 \frac{\Delta V}{\Delta t}$$

$$+ \text{Power losses}$$

In other words, the input power $p_1 Q_1$ from the pump is used to provide the output

power p_2Q_2 to the motor, overcome the power losses due to frictional effects, and provide the rate of change of potential and kinetic energies.
Therefore,

$$p_1Q_1 = \rho Q \frac{(v_2^2 - v_1^2)}{2} + g\rho Q (y_2 - y_1) + p_2Q_2$$ (1.14)

+ Power losses

EXAMPLE 1.2

Referring to Figure 1.4, assume that the pump delivers 18 MPa at a flow rate of 1.5×10^{-3} m³/s, into the pipe, but let the cross-sectional area be constant with an internal diameter of 20.9 mm. The pump is at ground reference and the motor is 3 m above it. Determine the expected output power from the motor. Assume the oil density to be 858.2 kg/m³, and no losses due to friction in the pipe.

Calculate the values of the various parts to equation (1.14),

Rate of change of PE $= g\rho Q (y_2 - y_1)$

$= 9.81 \times 858.2 \times 1.5 \times 10^{-3} \times 3$

$= 37.89$ W

Rate of change of KE $= \rho Q \left(\dfrac{v_2^2 - v_1^2}{2} \right)$

$= \dfrac{858.2 \times 1.5 \times 10^{-3}}{2} \times \left(\dfrac{1.5 \times 10^{-3}}{3.5 \times 10^{-4}} \right)^2$

$= 12.3$ W

Output power the pump $= 18 \times 10^6 \times 1.5 \times 10^6$

$= 27,000$ W

$$\text{Output power the motor} = 27\,000 - 37.89 - 12.32$$

$$= 26\,949.8 \text{ W}$$

Hence the KE and PE contribute very little in this case, so it is quite permissible to use simply,

Power Input = Power Output + Power Losses

The term hydrostatic refers to this situation, where the fluid's energy is more due to high pressure than to high velocity. The latter case is termed hydrokinetic.

Another important relationship is the continuity equation which states that for steady flow in a pipeline, the weight flow rate for gases, and the volume flow rate for liquids is the same for all cross-sections of the pipeline.

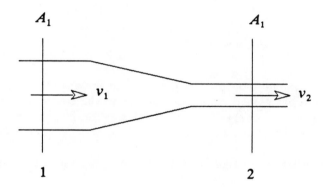

Figure 1.5 Continuity of Flow

Referring to Figure 1.5, the weight flows at sections 1 and 2 are equal,

$$W_1 = W_2 \tag{1.15}$$

or, particularly in the case of gases,

$$\rho_1 A_1 v_1 = \rho_2 A_2 v_2 \tag{1.16}$$

since the density changes with pressure, its value may not be the same at the two sections.

In the case of incompressible fluids the densities will be the same, and therefore,

$$A_1 v_1 = A_2 v_2 \qquad (1.17)$$

In other words, the smaller the pipe size, the greater the flow velocity and vice versa.

If the pipe is not sloped, then Bernoulli's equation can be written,

$$\frac{p_1}{\rho g} + \frac{v_1^2}{2g} = \frac{p_2}{\rho g} + \frac{v_2^2}{2g}$$

or,

$$p_1 - p_2 = \frac{\rho}{g} (v_2^2 - v_1^2) \qquad (1.18)$$

and, since $v_2 > v_1$, p_1 must be greater than p_2. In moving from position 1 to position 2, the fluid has gained kinetic energy due to the continuity equation, at the expense of pressure energy. A practical way of interpreting this is to remember that high flow rates are associated with low local pressures and vice versa.

If $v_2 >> v_1$, then there is a significant reduction in pipe section, and equation (1.18) reduces to,

$$Q = a v_2 = a \sqrt{\frac{2}{\rho}} \sqrt{p_1 - p_2} \qquad (1.19)$$

for ideal liquid flow. Experimental data show that the actual flow is about 65% of the value predicted by (1.19), so that for a typical hydraulic oil the design equation is,

$$Q = 0.65 \sqrt{\frac{2}{\rho}} a \sqrt{p_1 - p_2} = 3.12 \times 10^{-2} a \sqrt{p_1 - p_2} \ \text{m}^3/\text{s} \qquad (1.20)$$

This relationship can be used for an orifice. It will also be shown in Chapter 5, that for ideal gas flow through an orifice,

$$Q \propto \frac{a P_1}{\sqrt{T_1}} \qquad (1.21)$$

The practical implication of these equations is that leakage will be higher in pneumatic components than in components using liquids, because flow is directly proportional to upstream pressure in the case of gases. Some comparisons between the characterisics of the two fluids are shown in Table 1.7.

Table 1.7

Gas	Oil
Compressible	Incompressible
Systems have limited dynamic response	Systems have good dynamic response
Piston does not respond immediately after valve is opened	Piston responds immediately after valve is opened
Dry friction problems, due to air having poor lubricity	Lubrication not a problem Dominant viscous friction
No cavitation effects	Cavitation can occur
Can operate at very high temperature	Temperature range limited by fluid specification

EXAMPLE 1.3

A frictionless pipe has two orifices in series. The upstream orifice has a diameter of 3 mm. The upstream pressure is 12 MPa and 5 MPa is dropped across this orifice. If the end of the pipe is open, what must be the diameter of the second orifice?

Since the two orifices are in series, the flow must be common to both, and since the second orifice continues to an open-ended pipe, the final pressure must be at atmosphere, that is 0 Pa(g).

For each orifice we can use equation (1.20),

$$Q = 3.12 \times 10^{-2} a \sqrt{P_u - P_d}$$

Therefore,

$$a_1 \sqrt{P_1 - P_2} = a_2 \sqrt{P_2 - P_3} \qquad \text{where } P_3 = 0$$

$$a_2 = a_1 \sqrt{\frac{P_1 - P_2}{P_2}} = 7.06 \times 10^{-6} \sqrt{\frac{5 \times 10^6}{7 \times 10^6}} = 5.96 \times 10^{-6} \text{ m}^2$$

$$d_2 = 2.76 \text{ mm}$$

1.4 The gas laws

The compression and expansion of gases can be described by several relationships. The best known of these is Boyle's law which states that if a given mass of gas is compressed or expanded at a constant temperature, then the absolute pressure is inversely proportional to the volume,

$$P_1 V_1 = P_2 V_2 \tag{1.22}$$

If the absolute temperature is changed under constant pressure conditions, then we have Charles' Law,

$$\frac{V_1}{T_1} = \frac{V_2}{T_2} \tag{1.23}$$

and the third relationship is known as Gay Lussac's Law, for constant volume,

$$\frac{P_1}{T_1} = \frac{P_2}{T_2} \tag{1.24}$$

Combining (1.23) and (1.24) results in the Combined Gas Law.

Because the density of a gas is so sensitive to pressure and temperature changes, manufacturers often quote equipment specifications in terms of free air delivered (FAD),

$$p_1 \frac{V_1}{T_1} = p_2 \frac{V_2}{T_2} = \text{Constant} \tag{1.25}$$

this refers to the volume which the gas would occupy under standard air conditions of 101.3 kPa, 20°C and a relative humidity of 36%. Sometimes a temperature of 15.5°C is quoted; however the former is more commonly accepted.

EXAMPLE 1.4

An air tank has a volume of 0.15 m³ and is filled with compressed air at a pressure of 827.0 kPa(g), at a temperature of 115°F. The air is cooled to 70°F. What is the final pressure in the tank?

The tank is solid so the volume will remain fixed in this case. Applying (1.24), and converting the temperature to Kelvin,

$$p_2 = p_1 \frac{T_2}{T_1} = 928.3 \times \frac{294.26}{319.26} = 855.61 \text{ kPa(a)}$$

since, using absolute quantities,

$$p_1 = 827 + 101.3 = 928.3 \text{ kPa}$$

$$T_1 = \frac{(115 - 32)}{1.8} + 273.15 = 319.26 \text{ K}$$

EXAMPLE 1.5

Find the density of nitrogen gas at a pressure of 101.3 kPa and a temperature of 20°C. The molecular weight of nitrogen is given as 28.02.

First calculate the gas constant for nitrogen from the Universal gas constant given in Section 1.3.1,

$$R = \frac{R'}{\text{Mol Wt}} = \frac{8315}{28.02} = 297 \text{ J/kg.K}$$

$$T = 20 + 273.15$$

$$\rho = \frac{p}{RT} = \frac{101.3 \times 10^3}{297 \times 293.15} = 1.16 \text{ kg/m}^3$$

The expansion or compression of a gas is said to be isothermal if the temperature of the gas remains constant, that is, the conditions of Boyle's Law exist. It is only if the gas is allowed to expand freely without doing external work that these conditions truly exist. In practice, a good approximation is obtained by allowing the expansion or compression to occur slowly.

Adiabatic expansion or compression of a gas takes place if there is no heat loss during the process, and this is approximated in practice by the rapid expansion or compression of the gas. In this case we have the relationship,

$$pV^\gamma = K \tag{1.26}$$

$$\frac{pV^\gamma}{pV} = \frac{K}{mRT}$$

$$T = \frac{KV}{mRV^\gamma} = \frac{KV^{1-\gamma}}{mR} = \frac{K}{mR}\frac{1}{V^{\gamma-1}}$$

$$\frac{T_1}{T_2} = \left(\frac{V_1}{V_2}\right)^{1-\gamma} = \left(\frac{V_2}{V_1}\right)^{\gamma-1}$$

where $\gamma = C_p/C_v$ = ratio of specific heats.

The specific heat of any substance is defined as the amount of heat required to raise unit mass of that substance through 1° of temperature. For gases, we have to state the conditions under which the heating was applied, and this may be either under constant volume C_v or constant pressure C_p conditions. For air this ratio is taken as 1.4.

If p_1, V_1 are the initial conditions of an adiabtic process and p_2, V_2 are the final conditions, then it is easy to show that,

(a) To calculate temperature change,

$$T_1 = T_2 \left(\frac{V_2}{V_1} \right)^{\gamma - 1} = T_2 \left(\frac{p_1}{p_2} \right)^{\frac{(\gamma - 1)}{\gamma}} \tag{1.27a}$$

(b) To calculate pressure change,

$$P_1 = P_2 \left(\frac{V_2}{V_1} \right)^{\gamma} = P_2 \left(\frac{T_1}{T_2} \right)^{\frac{(\gamma - 1)}{\gamma}} \tag{1.27b}$$

(c) To calculate volume change,

$$V_1 = V_2 \left(\frac{p_2}{p_1} \right)^{\frac{1}{\gamma}} = V_2 \left(\frac{T_2}{T_1} \right)^{\frac{1}{(\gamma - 1)}} \tag{1.27c}$$

EXAMPLE 1.6

Consider two containers connected by a frictionless pipe and valve. With the valve closed, the first container is inflated with air to a pressure of 12.5 MPa(a) at 21°C. The temperature is then reduced slowly to −54 °C. The valve is opened so that there is a rapid discharge into the second chamber. The pressure drops to 5.5 MPa(a). If the second container has a volume of 0.819 l, what is the volume of the first container, and what will the temperature drop to when the process is completed?

At −54°C, assuming an isothermal process, the pressure in the first container will be,

$$P_2 = P_1 \frac{T_2}{T_1} = 12.5 \times 10^6 \times \frac{-54 + 273.15}{21 + 273.15} = 9.31 \text{ MPa}$$

if the first container has a volume V^a, then when the valve is opened we have a new container of volume $(V^a + 0.819 \times 10^{-3})$.

$$P_1(V^a)^\gamma = P_2(V^a + 0.819 \times 10^{-3})^\gamma$$

or,

$$(P_1)^{1/\gamma} V^a = (P_2)^{1/\gamma} (V^a + 0.819 \times 10^{-3})$$

$$V^a = \left(\frac{5.5 \times 10^6}{9.23 \times 10^6} \right)^{\frac{1}{1.4}} (V^a + 0.819 \times 10^{-3})$$

$$= 1.83 \times 10^{-3} \text{ m}^3$$

During this process the temperature will drop by an amount,

$$(273 - 54) = T_2 \left(\frac{2.649 \times 10^{-3}}{1.83 \times 10^{-3}} \right)^{0.4}$$

$$T_2 = 168.2 \text{ K} = -104.8°\text{C}$$

EXAMPLE 1.7

An 80 mm bore air cylinder is used to cushion the impact of a load travelling down an incline. If the cylinder is filled with compressed air at 380 kPa(g), and has a full stroke of 170 mm, calculate the length of the cushioning stroke, if the maximum pressure in the cylinder is limited to 1200 kPa(g).

In this case the process is clearly rapid, so if $p_1 V_1$ and $p_2 V_2$ are the initial and final conditions, respectively, then (1.27c) can be used. However the volume V_2 is a function of the cushioning stroke, x,

$$V_2 = \frac{\pi d^2}{4} (0.17 - x)$$

therefore,

$$\frac{\pi d^2}{4} \times (0.17 - x) = \frac{\pi d^2}{4} \times 0.17 \times \left(\frac{380 + 101.3}{1200 + 101.3} \right)^{\frac{1}{1.4}}$$

$$0.17 - x = 0.17 \times 0.491$$

$$x = 0.087 \text{ m}$$

It is sometime useful to work with the perfect gas relationship, instead of the Combined Gas Law.

EXERCISES

1.1. A hydraulic pipe has an outside diameter of 21.3 mm and a wall thickness of 2.75 mm. Oil is delivered at a constant flow rate of 101 l/min. The oil viscosity characteristics are,

Temperature °C	37.8	15.6
Viscosity Pa.s	2.8×10^{-2}	14×10^{-2}

At what temperature does the oil flow become turbulent?

1.2. A pipe delivers 4.0 kW of power to oil flowing at 2.25 l/s. The internal diameter of the pipe is 26.6 mm. The fluid is being pumped vertically through a distance of 7.6 m, measured from the surface of the oil in the tank, to the inlet to a ram. Calculate the pressure available at the inlet to the ram, if the head loss due to friction in the pipe is 9.6 m.

1.3. A tank used to hold hydraulic oil has an exit hole at the bottom. It is necessary to lower the liquid level from 3.5 to 1.5 m. If the capacitance of the tank, that is the ratio of the change in volume to a change in liquid level, is 3 m², how long will it take to drop the level? Assume $a\sqrt{2g} = 0.03$.

1.4. A hydraulic press consists of a large area ram of 15 cm internal diameter, connected to a smaller area ram of 1.25 cm internal diameter, by an oil-filled pipe. What is the magnitude of force which needs to be applied to the rod of the smaller ram to allow the larger ram raise a load of 1500 kg? If the small ram piston has a stroke of 25 cm, how many strokes would be needed to lift the load 1.5 m? If the time taken to lift the load is 15 min, what power is required? Ignore any effects due to friction and compressibility.

1.5. Air is used at a rate of 0.85 m³/min from a storage tank. The air pressure is 862 kPa(g) at a temperature of 32°C. If the atmospheric pressure and temperature are 101.3 kPa and 20°C, how many m³/min FAD, must the compressor provide?

1.6. A double-acting, double-ended air cylinder has a bore of 50.8 mm, a rod diameter of 25.4 mm and a stroke of 254 mm. What air compressor capacity is needed to operate the cylinder at 25 cycles /min, if the supply pressure is constant at 420 kPa(g)?

1.7. A storage tank is 2 m long and 0.7 m in diameter. It is filled with air, compressed at 0.7 MPa(g) at 26.6°C. A pneumatically operated production machine uses 0.6 m³ of free air delivered. Calculate the weight of air in the storage tank after 0.6 m³ of gas has been drawn off. What is the final pressure if the air temperature in the storage tank drops to 15.5°C?

CHAPTER 2

Dynamic behaviour in fluid power

2.1 Introduction

Design, in this text, means engineering calculations and analysis necessary to select and size components or systems. In order to optimize the designs of hydraulic and pneumatic equipment so that the best response times can be achieved, it is necessary to understand the parameters that affect performance.

A system is a collection of components acting together to perform a specific function. These components can be of one type or a mixture, such as electrical and hydraulic. However, they are normally connected in series and therefore the overall speed of response is dominated by the slowest component.

The basis for describing a system assumes a cause-effect relationship for the components, both individually and as a combination. In the early stages of design, it is convenient to represent a component by a block diagram. This avoids the complication of having to describe in detail the physical design of each part.

A component normally consists of several parts, and the usual procedure towards developing a mathematical model is to break the unit down gradually into more and more detailed parts as the model is improved.

A block diagram of a system is a pictorial representation of the function performed by each component and the direction of flow of the signals. All system variables are linked to each other through functional blocks and these terms are used in system simulation. Each block will have an equation relating to it, so that the output from each block is the input in that block, weighted or filtered by the equation. These equations are called transfer functions and are usually denoted by $G(s)$, which represents a multiplier or gain, and a time-dependent relationship.

When individual blocks are connected in series, they can often be represented by a single block containing the product of the transfer functions, as shown in Figure 2.1.

When the blocks are arranged in parallel, the transfer function outputs add together at a summing junction, as shown in Figure 2.2. This junction is denoted by a circle and the sign of each signal entering the circle is indicated. The direction of signal flow can be indicated by arrows. A point where a signal divides up into several signals is called a take-off point, and in the case of Figure 2.2, the paths are termed feedforward. Feedback is normally associated with the topic of automatic control, but many components have inherent feedback, for example the simple spring damper shown in Figure 2.9. At any feedback summing junction, the input signal is algebraically summed with one or more filtered output signals to produce an error signal. This arrangement is called a zero error seeking system. It is also convenient to use *H(s)* for feedback transfer function; a typical example is shown in Figure 2.3.

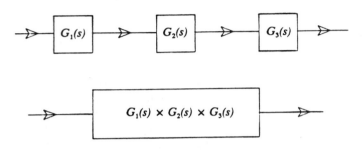

Figure 2.1 Blocks in Series

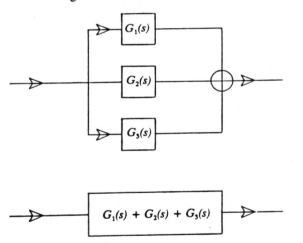

Figure 2.2 Blocks in Parallel

The relationship between the output *O(s)* and the input *I(s)* is obtained by manipulating the blocks,

Feedforward Path,

$$O(s) = [G_1(s)][G_2(s)]E(s)$$

Summing Junction,

$$E(s) = I(s) - O'(s)$$

Feedback Path,

$$O'(s) = [H_1(s)]O(s)$$

Hence,

$$E(s) = I(s) - [H_1(s)]O(s)$$

$$O(s) = [G_1](s)][G_2(s)][I(s)-[H_1(s)]O(s)]$$

$$\frac{O(s)}{I(s)} = \frac{[G_1(s)][G_2(s)]}{1 + [G_1(s)][G_2(s)][H_1(s)]} \qquad (2.1)$$

The advantage of using block diagrams lies in the fact that it is easy to form the overall block diagram for the whole system by connecting the blocks representing the components according to the signal flow direction.

Often, the exercise of formulating the diagram helps the modeller to understand the physical behaviour of the device, and it is also possible to evaluate the contributions of each component to the overall performance of the system.

EXAMPLE 2.1

Reduce the block diagram shown in Figure 2.4, and find the transfer function between x_i and x_o.

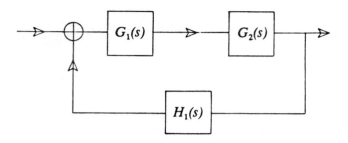

Figure 2.3   Feedback Arrangement

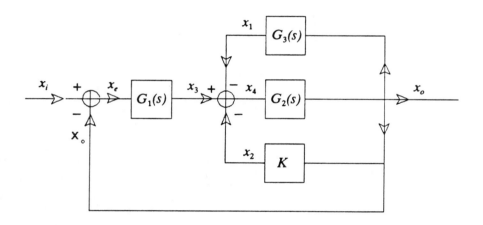

Figure 2.4   For Worked Example 2.1

Consider the inner loop containing K, $G_2(s)$ and $G_3(s)$ first,

$$x_4 = x_3 - x_1 - x_2$$

$$= x_3 - G_3(s)x_o - Kx_o$$

giving,

$$x_o = G_2(s)x_4$$

$$= G_2(s)[x_3 - G_3(s)x_o - Kx_o]$$

$$= G_2(s)[x_3 - (G_3(s) + K)x_o]$$

hence,

$$x_o = \frac{G_2(s)}{1 + G_2(s)(G_3(s) + K)} x_3$$

but,

$$x_e = x_i - x_o$$

$$x_o = \left[\frac{G_2(s)}{1 + G_2(s)(G_3(s) + K)} G_1(s) \right] x_e$$

$$= \left[\frac{G_2(s)G_1(s)}{1 + G_2(s)(G_3(s) + K)} \right] (x_i - x_e)$$

$$= [A]x_i - [A]x_o$$

Therefore,

$$x_o = \frac{[A]}{1 + [A]} x_i$$

$$= \frac{\dfrac{G_2(s)G_1(s)}{1 + G_2(s)(G_3(s) + K)}}{1 + \dfrac{G_2(s)G_1(s)}{1 + G_2(s)(G_3(s) + K)}} x_i$$

$$x_o = \frac{G_2(s)G_1(s)}{1 + G_2(s)(G_3(s) + K) + G_2(s)G_1(s)} x_i$$

$$= \frac{G_2(s)G_1(s)}{1 + G_2(s)(G_3(s) + G_1(s) + K)} x_i$$

2.2 Conceptual modelling

A mathematical model for any mechanical system can be developed by applying Newton's Laws. The three basic lumped parameter elements used are mass and inertia elements, spring elements and damper elements.

(a) Mass and inertia elements

This covers both mass in linear motion and moment of inertia related to rotational motion, and represents all the mass distributed throughout the moving part by a single lump.

$$\text{Mass} = \frac{\text{Force}}{\text{Acceleration}} \quad \frac{\text{N}}{\text{m}}/\text{s}^2 \ \textit{or} \ \text{kg}$$

$$F = m\frac{d^2x}{dt^2} = m\frac{dv}{dt} \tag{2.2}$$

$$v = m\int F dt$$

In the case of rotation,

$$\text{Moment of Inertia} = \frac{\text{Torque}}{\text{Angular Acceleration}} \quad \text{kg m}^2$$

$$T = I\frac{d^2\theta}{dt^2} = I\frac{d\omega}{dt} \tag{2.3}$$

The mass element is an energy storage device, storing energy by virtue of its kinetic energy, and inductance is the electrical equivalent.

(b) Spring elements

A linear spring is a mechanical element that can be deformed by an external force. The element can be either stretched or subjected to torsion,

$$\text{Spring Rate} = \frac{\text{Force}}{\text{Deflection}} \quad \text{N.m}$$

$$F = k(x_1 - x_2)$$

$$F = k\int(v_1 - v_2)\, dt \tag{2.4}$$

In the case of torsion,

$$T = k(\theta_1 - \theta_2) \tag{2.5}$$

The spring is also an energy storage element, and stores energy by virtue of its potential energy. The reciprocal of the spring rate is called compliance. This element is the equivalent of electrical capacitance which also stores energy.

(c) Damper elements

A damper is a mechanical element that dissipates energy in the form of heat. For a translational element, the generated damping force is proportional to velocity,

$$\text{Damping Rate} = \frac{\text{Force}}{\text{Velocity}} \quad \frac{\text{N.s}}{\text{m}}$$

$$F = b(v_1 - v_2) \tag{2.6}$$

In the case of torsion,

$$\text{Torsional Damping Rate} = \frac{\text{Torque}}{\text{Angular Velocity}} \quad \frac{\text{N.m.s}}{\text{rad}} \tag{2.7}$$

$$T = b(\alpha_1 - \alpha_2)$$

The coefficient b is called the viscous damping coefficient and should not be confused with the damping ratio. There is another type of friction commonly found in mechanical systems: dry or Coulomb friction. This will provide damping to a system which is independent of velocity and therefore is non-linear.

The lumped parameter approach provides ideal models, since for example a spring exhibits only stiffness. In practice, a spring has mass and a low level of damping, but is assumed to be an element in which stiffness is the dominant characteristic.

Systems in general consist of inputs, and outputs (Figure 2.5), but there can also be external disturbances over which the designer has little control. Environmental temperature, humidity and electrical disturbances are some examples.   One objective is therefore to minimize their effect on the performance of the system.

The three lumped parameter elements discussed are summarized further in Table 2.1. It is seen that it is usual to express the equation for each element in terms of force and velocity. This is because the product of these two variables is power which flows through the system components,

$$W = F \times v \quad \text{N.m/s} \quad (\text{watts}) \tag{2.8}$$

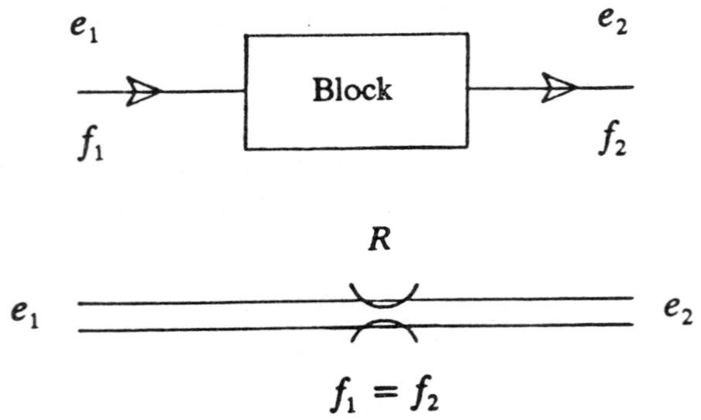

Figure 2.5 Block Diagram for an Orifice

The relationships can be expressed in either derivative or integral form, referred to as causality, but the latter is usually preferred.

In general (Figure 2.5), a model will have power flowing into it and power flowing out of it. Power is the product of two variables, one of which is called the effort variable e and the other the flow variable f. The entry and exit points of power flow are called ports.

Table 2.1

Element	Derivative Form	Integral Form
Mass	$F = m\, dv/dt$	$v = 1/m \int F\, dt$
Spring	$v = 1/k\, dF/dt$	$F = k \int v\, dt$
Damper	$F = bv$ or $v\, 1/bF$ either form acceptable	

$$\text{Power} = e \times f = dE/dt$$

and
$$\text{Efficiency} = \text{power out/power in}$$

The ratio of the effort variable, divided by the flow variable, is called the impedance of the port. So in the case of Figure 2.2,

$$\text{Input Impedance} = e_1/f_1$$

$$\text{Output Impedance} = e_2/f_2$$

In other words, this is a measure of the resistance to the flow of energy through a port. The inverse ratio is called the admittance. Impedance can be real or complex, depending on the system.

If the condition $f_1 = f_2 = f$ exists for the model shown in Figure 2.5, then,

$$e_2/e_1 = e_2/f \times f/e_1$$

which is called the transfer function. Note that cause and effect are associated with the causality of the model, and either can take on the role as an effort or a flow.

2.2.1 Causality

The key to any successful modelling is a clear understanding of the physical meaning of the process, so that the cause and effect can be correctly assigned to each effort or flow.

The first thing to recognize is that cause is the independant variable, whilst the effect is the dependent variable. Referring to Table 2.1, it can be seen that, for the mass element, the integral form shows that the force is the cause and the velocity the effect. Force is, of course, an effort variable, although some schools of thought prefer to define it as a flow variable. It does not really matter, provided that the declaration is made.

In the physical sense, a force is normally applied to a mass, with the result of accelerating it. Hence the integral form models the behaviour more realistically (Figure 2.6).

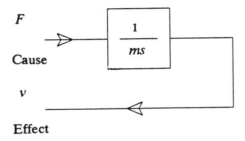

Figure 2.6   Mass Integral Causality

A spring in the integral form shows velocity, a flow variable, to be the cause, and in practice this implies that you deflect a spring to produce a force. However, it is just as meaningful to apply a force to a spring to cause a deflection.

The model selected is sometimes not quite as straightforward in these cases; it depends on the situation (Figure 2.7). The damping element can also be defined in either integral or derivative form.

2.2.2 Analogies

A signal, element or system which exhibits behaviour mathematically identical to that of another physically different signal, element or system is called an analog. It is recognized, for example, that pressure is analogous to voltage, and flow is analogous to current. Familiarity with these connections can often be very helpful to the engineer in model formulation. A summary of analogous relationships

A summary of analogous relationshipsis given in Table 2.2.

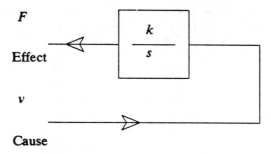

Figure 2.7 Stiffness, Integral Causality

There is a special case with thermodynamic analogies, since heat flow is already an energy flow, with the units of power, while temperature has no units. However, the product of these two variables is still power.

2.3 Modelling methods and transfer functions

It is not sufficient to have only a knowledge of the physical behaviour of a system, it is also essential to have mathematical techniques to allow the manipulation of expressions describing the behaviour of the system. Such mathematical expressions are termed transfer function, and show the relationship between the input and output across a system. The test for a linear system is that when a sinusoidal signal is applied to the input, the output from the system should have the same frequency. There can, however, be a change in the ratio of the output to input amplitudes as the frequency is increased. There can also be a change in the phase angle (Figure 2.8).

In order to examine the dynamic behaviour of such systems, it is necessary to be able to express the phase angle and amplitude ratio in mathematical terms. The vehicle for this is the transfer function, which in turn is obtained by writing the differential equation for the relationship between the output and input.

2.3.1 First order models

Consider a simple spring and damping device as shown in Figure 2.9. If the top of the spring, at x, is reciprocated slowly, then the bottom, at y, will follow the movement. As the frequency of the reciprocation is increased, then the restraining force associated with the damper is increased, and consequently the movement of the bottom of the spring is restricted. Hence, this component allows low-frequency motion to be transmitted, but higher frequency motion to be blocked or filtered out. This is a description of the the physical behaviour of a device that functions as a low pass filter.

Table 2.2

	Effort	Flow	$\int (f)\, dt$	$\int (e)\, dt$
General	e	f	q = displacement	p = momentum
Electrical	V	i	q = charge	λ = flux linkage
Mechanical	F	v	x = displacement	p = momentum
	T	ω	θ = angle	L = angular momentum
Fluids	P	Q	V = volume	Φ = pressure momentum
Thermal	T	$ds\,/dt$	s = entropy	

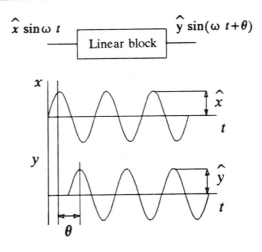

Figure 2.8 Time Response of a Linear System

Now build the mathematical model by considering the force present when x is depressed,

$$\text{Spring force} = k(x - y)$$

$$\text{Damping force} = b\frac{dy}{dt}$$

(2.9)

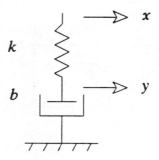

Figure 2.9 Simple Spring Damper

These forces must balance,

$$k(x - y) = b\,\frac{dy}{dt}$$

$$x = \frac{b}{k}\frac{dy}{dt} + y$$

(2.10)

This is a first-order linear differential equation, so a low pass filter is represented by a first-order model. The block diagram can be drawn by rearranging equation (2.10), so that the highest derivative is on the left side of the equation,

$$b\,\frac{dy}{dt} = kx - ky$$

Figure 2.10 shows the resulting block diagram, and illustrates that even this simple component has an inherent feedback loop.

If a unit step change is applied to the input x, then the solution to equation (2.10) gives,

$$y = 1 - e^{-t/T} \qquad\qquad (2.11)$$

where $T = b/k$ and is called the Time Constant; notice that it has the units of time.

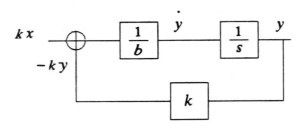

Figure 2.10 Block Diagram of Simple Spring Damper

Figure 2.11 shows the plot for equation (2.11), and is the time response. This model reveals that a first-order system is characterized by an exponential response that reaches 63.2% of its steady-state value when $t = T$ and steady state is taken as $4T$, although in theory it is when t reaches infinity.

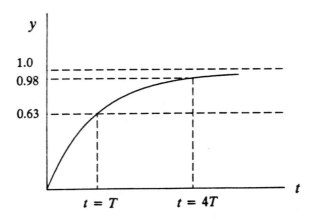

Figure 2.11 Response of a First-Order System

The speed of response can then be adjusted by either changing the spring stiffness or the damping rate.

EXAMPLE 2.2

The outflow of oil from a tank, 0.6 m in diameter, is proportional to the head of oil in the tank. A ball valve operated by the liquid level regulates the inflow to $0.051\, x$ m³/s, where x is the fall in level below the desired value of 2 m. If the shut-off valve in the outflow pipe is suddenly opened so that the outflow changes from zero to $0.0046\, h$ m³/s, where h is the actual level in the vessel, determine:

(a) The steady-state value of the oil level in the tank.

(b) The time taken for the level in the tank to fall 80 mm.

(a) The inflow to the tank is,

$$Q_i = 0.051\,(2 - h)$$

When the outlet valve is opened,

$$Q_o = 0.0046\, h$$

For the oil level to remain steady, the outflow and inflow must be identical, hence,

$$0.0046\, h = 0.051\,(2 - h)$$

$$h = 1.82 \text{ m}$$

(b) If a steady-state condition has not been reached, then the difference between the inflow and outflow must account for the change in level,

$$0.051(2 - h) - 0.0046h = \frac{\pi(0.6)^2}{4} \times \frac{dh}{dt}$$

$$(0.283s + 0.056)h = 0.102$$

The transient behaviour of this first-order equation can by found by considering the complementary function.

Set the right-hand side of the equation to zero and assume that,

$$h = A e^{\alpha t}$$

is a solution to the equation,

$$0.283 \alpha + 0.056 = 0$$

$$\alpha = -0.198$$

hence,

$$h = A e^{-0.198t}$$

The complete solution is the sum of the steady-state and transient solutions,

$$h = 1.82 + A e^{-0.198t}$$

It is now necessary to find a value for the constant A. The boundary conditions are when $t=0$, $h=2$ m,

$$2 = 1.82 + A$$

$$A = 0.18$$

and therefore,

$$h = 1.82 + 0.18\, e^{-0.198t}$$

If the level of oil in the tank falls by 80 mm, then the time taken will be,

$$2 - 0.08 = 1.82 + 0.18\, e^{-0.198t}$$

$$e^{-0.198t} = 0.56$$

$$t = 2.9 \ s$$

2.3.2 First-order frequency response

To find the equivalent frequency response, suppose again that the top of the spring is subject to a sinusoidal motion at frequency ω rad/s,

$$x(t) = x' \sin(\omega\, t)$$

then the output y at the bottom of the spring will be,

$$y(t) = y' \sin(\omega\, t + \theta)$$

where θ represents any phase shift between the input and output motion that might be present see (Figure 2.8).

Equation (2.10) can be rewritten as,

$$x' \sin(\omega\, t) = \frac{b}{k}\frac{d}{dt} y' \sin(\omega\, t + \theta) + y' \sin(\omega\, t + \theta)$$

$$= \frac{b}{k} y' \omega\, \cos(\omega\, t + \theta) + y' \sin(\omega\, t + \theta) \qquad (2.12)$$

$$= \frac{b}{k} y' \omega j \sin(\omega\, t + \theta) + y' \sin(\omega\, t + \theta)$$

since the imaginary number j rotates a vector by 90°. Hence the frequency response function between the input and the output can be written,

$$\frac{y}{x} = \frac{1}{1 + \dfrac{b}{k}\omega j} \qquad (2.13)$$

Comparing equations (2.10) and (2.13), it is seen that d/dt in the time domain can be replaced by ωj in the frequency domain. The Laplace variable s is normally used for the transfer function format, so that equation (2.13) is expressed as,

$$\frac{y}{x}(s) = \frac{1}{1 + Ts} \qquad (2.14)$$

A very non-rigorous justification for these relationships, which can help in the understanding, is as follows. It is well known that,

$$e^{j\theta} = \cos\theta + j\sin\theta$$
$$\qquad\qquad\qquad\qquad\qquad\qquad (2.15)$$
$$e^{-j\theta} = \cos\theta - j\sin\theta$$

where $e^{j\theta}$ represents a unit vector which can be rotated counter-clockwise by an angle θ from the real axis of the complex plane. Hence,

For $\theta = 0$ $\qquad e^{j0} = e^0 = 1.0$

For $\theta = 90^o$ $\qquad e^{j90^o} = j = \sqrt{-1}$

For $\theta = 180^o$ $\qquad e^{j180^o} = e^{j90^o} \times e^{j90^o} = -1$

Hence the imaginary number j rotates a vector by 90°. If the input is a sine wave,

$$x = x'\sin(\omega t)$$

then,

$$\frac{dx}{dt} = x'\omega \cos(\omega t)$$

$$\frac{d^2x}{dt^2} = -x'\omega^2 \sin(\omega t) = -\omega^2 x = (\omega j)^2 x$$

Hence we can conclude that,

$$\frac{d^2}{dt^2} = (\omega j)^2$$

$$\frac{d}{dt} = (\omega j) = s$$

(2.16)

If we now substitute this into equation (2.14), we end up with equation (2.13). Notice that the denominator is a complex number with frequency as the variable. The units for ω are rads/s and the conversion to Hertz (Hz) is, $f = \omega / 2\pi$.

Converting equation (2.13) into a more manageable form,

$$\frac{Y}{x}(\omega j) = \frac{1}{1 + T\omega j} \times \frac{1 - T\omega j}{1 - T\omega j}$$

$$= \frac{1}{1 + \omega^2 T^2} - \frac{T\omega}{1 + \omega^2 T^2}$$

(2.17)

Hence the amplitude of the frequency response will be,

$$\left|\frac{y}{x}\right| = \sqrt{\left(\frac{1}{1 + \omega^2 T^2}\right)^2 + \left(\frac{T\omega}{1 + \omega^2 T^2}\right)^2}$$

$$= \frac{1}{\sqrt{1 + \omega^2 T^2}}$$

(2.18)

and,

$$dB = 20 \log_{10} \left| \frac{y}{x} \right|$$

The phase angle will be determined at each frequency from,

$$\theta = \tan^{-1}(-T\omega) \tag{2.19}$$

The negative sign in equation (2.19), indicates that the output lags behind the input. Figure 2.12 shows the results for a first-order lag with $T = 1.0$, over a range of frequencies.

This plot is called a Bode diagram by control engineers and a frequency response function plot by vibration engineers. In either case, linear log paper is used. One advantage is to compress the frequency scale so that plots over a wide frequency range can be condensed to a reasonable size. A second advantage is that reponse plots on linear log paper for several transfer functions in series can then use addition in place of multiplication and subtraction in place of division [4]. Important points to note are:

1. Drawing asymptotes as shown in Figure 2.12, the point where they intersect is called the break frequency, the reciprocal of which is the time constant, $T = 1/\omega_b$.

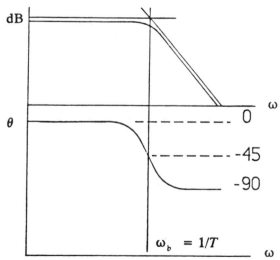

Figure 2.12 First-Order Frequency Response

2. The phase angle ranges from $0°$ at $\omega = 0$ to a maximum of $-90°$ at $\omega = \infty$. When $\omega = \omega_b$, the phase angle is $-45°$.

2.3.3 Second-order models

If a mass is added to the spring and damper considered in the previous section, the dynamic behaviour changes quite dramatically. A typical arrangement is shown in Figure 2.13.

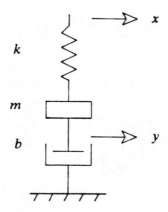

Figure 2.13 Spring Mass Damper

In this case, the input is the applied force and the output is the resultant displacement. The force required to accelerate the mass is,

$$F_m = m \, \frac{d^2y}{dt^2}$$

The damping force provided by the damper is,

$$F_b = -b \frac{dy}{dt}$$

The spring force, as a result of the deflection across it is,

$$F_k = k(x - y)$$

When the device is undergoing free vibrations, there is a force balance such that,

$$m\frac{d^2y}{dt} = -b\frac{dy}{dt} + k(x - y)$$

$$kx = m\frac{d^2y}{dt} + b\frac{dy}{dt} + ky$$

(2.20)

From this equation, the block diagram in Figure 2.14 can be drawn.

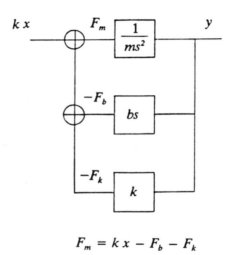

$$F_m = kx - F_b - F_k$$

Figure 2.14 Block Diagram of a Second-Order System

The simplest solution to equation (2.20), is for the case of free vibrations, where the input driving force is set to zero. As a trial solution let,

$$y(t) = Ae^{\alpha t}$$

and substituting this into equation (2.20) results in,

$$m\alpha^2 + b\alpha + k = 0$$

The term α is called a root of the equation, and in this case there are two roots or eigenvalues given by,

$$\alpha_{1,2} = \frac{-b \pm \sqrt{b^2 - 4mk}}{2m} \tag{2.21}$$

Hence the complete solution is of the form,

$$y(t) = C_1 e^{\alpha_1 t} + C_2 e^{\alpha_2 t} \tag{2.22}$$

This solution contains only exponential terms and is called the complementary function, since it describes the transient behaviour between two states. When the input is not set to zero, the steady-state solution is also required. The complete solution is therefore the sum of the complementary function and the particular integral.

Equation (2.21) shows that the type of response obtained will depend on the form of the terms within the square root.

(a) If the terms within the square root sum to zero, then the system is said to be critically damped, and,

$$b_c = 2\sqrt{km} \tag{2.23}$$

This is the value of damping that forms the boundary between an exponential response and an oscillatory response.

(b) If the terms within the square root sum to a positive value, then the system is said to be overdamped and will exhibit an exponential response.

(c) If the terms within the square root sum to a negative number, then the system said to be underdamped and will exhibit an oscillatory response.

The ratio of the spring stiffness k, divided by the mass m, is a fixed label for the lumped parameter model, termed the natural frequency. This will normally be fixed and represents the frequency at which the device would freely oscillate if the damping effects were zero.

$$\omega_n = \sqrt{\frac{k}{m}} \quad \text{rads/s}$$

$$f_n = \frac{1}{2\pi}\sqrt{\frac{k}{m}} \quad \text{Hz}$$

(2.24)

Another parameter often used is the damping ratio ζ, which is a measure of how far the actual damping is removed from critical damping. Critical damping is the amount of damping needed to just prevent a system oscillating in free vibrations.

$$\zeta = \frac{b}{b_c} = \frac{b}{2\sqrt{km}}$$

(2.25)

Hence, equation (2.20) can be rewritten in a more general form as,

$$x = \frac{1}{\omega_n^2}\frac{d^2y}{dt^2} + \frac{2\zeta}{\omega_n}\frac{dy}{dt} + y$$

(2.26)

and the roots of the equation given in (2.12) become,

$$\alpha_{1,2} = -\zeta\omega_n \pm \omega_n\sqrt{1-\zeta^2}j$$

(2.27)

for the underdamped condition. This case occurs frequently in the design of fluid power systems, since they are generally inherently underdamped.

The term $\omega_n\sqrt{(1-\zeta^2)}$ in equation (2.27) is known as the frequency of damped vibrations. For this case, the complete solution, using equation (2.22), becomes,

$$y(t) = C_1 e^{(-\zeta\omega_n + j\omega_d)t} + C_2 e^{(-\zeta\omega_n - j\omega_d)t}$$

Referring to equations (2.16), as used in complex number manipulation,

$$y(t) = e^{-\zeta\omega_n t}([C_1 + C_2]\cos\omega_d t + j[C_1 - C_2]\sin\omega_d t) \qquad (2.28)$$

Since the displacement $y(t)$ is a real physical quantity, then $(C_1 + C_2)$ and $j(C_1 - C_2)$ must also be real, and C_1 and C_2 must be complex conjugates. Therefore,

$$y(t) = e^{-\zeta\omega_n t}(A_1 \cos\omega_d t + A_2 \sin\omega_d t) \qquad (2.29)$$

here A_1 and A_2 are arbitrary constants depending on the applied initial conditions. For example, if the intial conditions are that at $t = 0$; $y(0) = y_0$ and $v(0) = v_0$, then,

$$A_1 = y_o \qquad \text{and} \qquad A_2 = \frac{v_o o + \zeta y_o \omega_n}{\omega_d} \qquad (2.30)$$

As an alternative approach, let

$$A_1 = C \cos\theta \qquad \text{and} \qquad A_2 = -C \sin\theta$$

then equation (2.29) can be rewritten as,

$$y(t) = Ce^{-\zeta\omega_n t}(\cos\theta\cos\omega_d t + \sin\theta\sin\omega_d t)$$
$$= Ce^{-\zeta\omega_n t}\cos(\omega_d t + \theta) \qquad (2.31)$$

But if each expression in equation (2.30) is squared and summed then,

$$C^2 (\sin^2\theta + \cos^2\theta) = A_1^2 + A_2^2$$

$$C = \sqrt{A_1^2 + A_2^2}$$

and the phase angle θ is given by,

$$\theta = \tan^{-1}\left(-\frac{A_2}{A_1}\right)$$

EXAMPLE 2.3

A second-order spring mass damper is deflected by a unit displacement at $t = 0$, then released. Find an expression for the response. The initial conditions are that at $t = 0$, $y(0) = 1.0$ and $v(0) = 0$. The arbitrary constants are,

$$A_1 = y(0) = 1.0$$

$$A_2 = \frac{v(0) + \zeta y(0)\omega_n}{\omega_d}$$

$$= \frac{\zeta\omega_n}{\omega_d} = \frac{\zeta}{\sqrt{1-\zeta^2}}$$

$$C = \sqrt{A_1^2 + A_2^2} = \sqrt{1 + \frac{\zeta^2}{1-\zeta^2}}$$

$$= \frac{1}{\sqrt{1-\zeta^2}}$$

$$\theta = \tan^{-1}\left(-\frac{\zeta}{\sqrt{1-\zeta^2}}\right)$$

Therefore using equation (2.31),

$$y(t) = \frac{1}{\sqrt{1 - \zeta^2}} e^{-\zeta \omega_n t} \cos\left[\omega_d t + \tan^{-1}\left(\frac{\zeta}{\sqrt{1 - \zeta^2}}\right)\right]$$

Figure 2.15 shows a typical plot for this expression, for $\omega = 10$ rad/s and $\zeta = 0.01$.

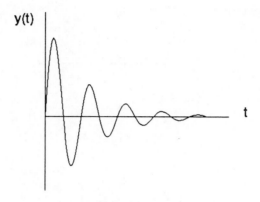

Figure 2.15 Time Domain Response

2.3.4 Second-order frequency response

The procedure for determining the frequency response is similiar to that used for the first-order system. Therefore equation (2.20) can be rewritten as,

$$\frac{y}{x} = \frac{k}{ms^2 + bs + k}$$

which can be expressed in more general form (see equation (2.26)) as,

$$\frac{y}{x} = \frac{\omega_n^2}{s^2 + 2\zeta\omega_n s + \omega_n^2}$$

and since $s \equiv \omega j$,

$$\frac{y}{x} = \frac{\omega_n^2}{\omega_n^2 - \omega^2 + 2\zeta\omega_n\omega j}$$

resulting in an amplitude response given by,

$$\left|\frac{y}{x}\right| = \frac{1}{\sqrt{\left[1 - \left(\frac{\omega}{\omega_n^2}\right)^2\right]^2 + 4\zeta^2\left[\frac{\omega}{\omega_n}\right]^2}} \tag{2.32}$$

and a phase angle of,

$$\theta = \tan^{-1} - \left(\frac{2\zeta\dfrac{\omega}{\omega_n}}{1 - \left(\dfrac{\omega}{\omega_n}\right)^2}\right) \tag{2.33}$$

When the damping ratio is less than 1.0, a maximum occurs in the response plot (Figure 2.16) at the resonant frequency. Hence, if equation (2.32) is differentiated with respect to (ω /ω_n) and set equal to zero, the condition that results is,

$$-4\frac{\omega}{\omega_n}\left[1 - \left(\frac{\omega}{\omega_n}\right)^2\right] + 8\zeta^2\left(\frac{\omega}{\omega_n}\right) = 0$$

$$\omega = \omega_r = \omega_n\sqrt{1 - 2\zeta^2}$$

This should not be confused with a very similiar relationship for the frequency of damped oscillations.

The characteristics for a second-order system are:

1. The natural frequency occurs when the phase angle is $-90°$.

2. The shape of the response is controlled by the value of the damping ratio.

3. The resonant frequency occurs at the peak in the response curve and its height is controlled by the damping ratio.

4. The amplitude response falls off at -12 dB/oct after the resonant peak.

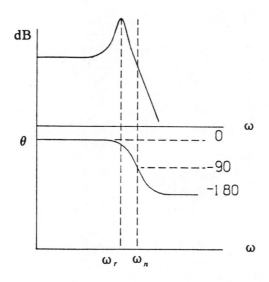

Figure 2.16 Second-Order Frequency Response

EXERCISES

2.1. A hydraulic component, shown in Figure 2.17, consists of flow being divided between an orifice of resistance R and a spring-loaded piston.

 (a) Find the relationship between the piston movement y, and the input flow Q_1.

 (b) Sketch the expected frequency response.

2.2. A system of components is found to be arranged as shown in Figure 2.18. If,

$$k = 10, \qquad\qquad H_1(s) = 4s$$

$$G_1(s) = \frac{8}{s(s+2)(s+3)}, \qquad H_2(s) = \frac{2}{(1+4s)}$$

(a) Find the relationship between the output y and the input x.

(b) What is the steady-state value of y/x ?

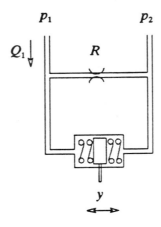

Figure 2.17 For Exercise 2.1

2.3. A process consists of two tanks, as shown in Figure 2.19. The capacitance of each tank is defined as the ratio of the change in quantity of liquid to the change in level. Note that the capacity of a tank is the actual volume. If the flow into the top tank is Q_3, find the relationship between this flow and the level in the second tank. The flow out of each tank is controlled by orifices of resistance R_1 and R_2.

2.4. Find the expression representing the time history of x, if the system represented by the equation shown is subjected to a step input $f(t)$ of unity. The boundary conditions are such that when $t = 0$, both x and dx/dt are zero.

$$450\frac{d^2x}{dt} + 105\frac{dx}{dt} + 10x = f(t)$$

2.5. A hydraulic motor has to produce a torque of 27 N.m for each radian of

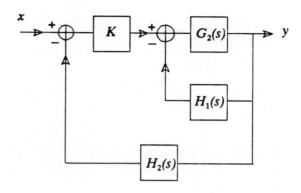

Figure 2.18 For Exercise 2.2

swash plate angle (see Figure 6.4a). The output shaft drives a load consisting of 1.4 kg.m^2 of inertia, and a damping coefficient of 4 N.m.s/rad.

(a) Calculate the damping ratio.

(b) Plot the Bode diagram of the shaft angle against swash plate angle.

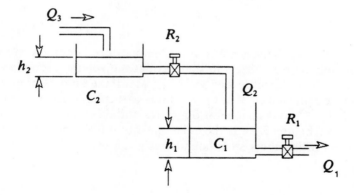

Figure 2.19 For Exercise 2.3

CHAPTER 3

Fluid compressibility and its effects

3.1 Compressibility

When a quantity of fluid occupies a volume V_1 at atmospheric pressure and V_2 at a pressure p_2, the reduction in volume expressed as a fraction of the original volume is termed the compression,

$$\text{Volume Reduction} = \frac{V_1 - V_2}{V_1}$$

In addition, when compression occurs, the fluid density increases,

$$\text{Density Reduction} = \frac{\rho_2 - \rho_1}{\rho_2}$$

As the fluid is compressed, there is also a local temperature increase, causing a small expansion in volume that offsets to some extent the volume reduction due to pressure increase. Hence, compression will be greater if the fluid is compressed isothermally than if compressed adiabatically. This is particularly relevant in gases or liquid/gas mixtures. Consider the mass flow rates of fluid entering and leaving a system, as shown in Figure 3.1. If the rates are not equal, then there is an accumulation of mass within the system boundaries given by,

$$\frac{dm_1}{dt} - \frac{dm_2}{dt} = \frac{dm}{dt} \tag{3.1}$$

56

Now since $m = \rho V$, equation (3.1) can be rewritten as,

$$\frac{dm_1}{dt} - \frac{dm_2}{dt} = \rho \frac{\partial V}{\partial t} + V \frac{\partial \rho}{\partial t} \qquad (3.2)$$

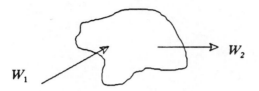

Figure 3.1 General Compressibility Model

For a liquid, the effects of pressure on density are not so important and the mass flow can be replaced by volume flow, since,

$$\frac{dm}{dt} = \rho \frac{dV}{dt} = \rho Q$$

Hence equation (3.1) becomes,

$$Q_1 - Q_2 = \frac{\partial V}{\partial t} + \frac{V}{\rho} \frac{\partial \rho}{\partial t} \qquad (3.3)$$

The first term represents the steady-state flow, and the second term is due to the compressibility effects. For convenience, the definition of fluid bulk modulus is introduced. If the pressure on a fluid volume V is increased by dp, it will cause a decrease in volume dV, and the fluid will increase in density. This is expressed by,

$$N = dp \Big/ \frac{-dV}{V} = -V \frac{dp}{dt} \qquad (3.4)$$

The bulk modulus of elasticity of a fluid is a measure of its resistance to reduction in volume under pressure. Compressibility is defined as the reciprocal of bulk modulus.

Now since,

$$V = \frac{m}{\rho}$$

$$\frac{dV}{d\rho} = -\frac{m}{\rho^2}$$

and converting equation (3.4),

$$N = -V\frac{dp}{dV} = -V\frac{dp}{d\rho}\frac{d\rho}{dV} = -\frac{m}{\rho}-\frac{\rho^2}{m}\frac{dp}{d\rho}$$

$$= \rho\frac{dp}{d\rho} \tag{3.5}$$

$$\frac{1}{N} = C = \frac{1}{\rho}\frac{d\rho}{dt}$$

Equation (3.3) can now be expressed in a more useful form as,

$$Q_1 - Q_2 = \frac{\partial V}{\partial t} + V\frac{1}{\rho}\frac{\partial \rho}{\partial p}\frac{\partial p}{\partial t}$$

$$= \frac{\partial V}{\partial t} + \frac{V}{N}\frac{\partial p}{\partial t} \tag{3.6}$$

which shows that the flow due to the compressibility term is dependent on the rate of change of pressure. As a result of this, when pressure is increased on a fluid volume V within a rigid chamber, additional volume is needed to be pumped into it; although this volume may be quite small, if the pressure change is rapid, then quite large flows are demanded for short periods. The transient flow Q_t is in fact the second term of equation (3.6), so that,

$$Q_t = \frac{V}{N}\frac{d(p_1-p_2)}{dt} \tag{3.7}$$

The time required to build up pressure during compressibility can be taken as between 0.03 and 0.05 s.

A wide range of oil bulk modulus values are available from manufacturers of the different types of fluids, so that at operating temperatures of around 46°C, oil free from entrained air can have values ranging from 13.78×10^8 Pa to 19.0×10^8 Pa at atmospheric pressure. These figures change with percentage of entrained air and operating pressure.

It is impossible to avoid air being entrained into the oil and this has the effect of lowering the bulk modulus. However, air dissolved in the liquid has very little effect on the modulus value. In 1951, it was shown by Rendel and Allan [5] and later corrected by Hayward [6] that the modified bulk modulus could be determined from,

$$N_e = \frac{1 + \dfrac{p_o V_a}{p V_f}}{1 + \dfrac{N p_o V_a}{p_2 V_f}}$$

where V_a is the volume of free air at p_o, and V_f is the volume of oil at p_o. A typical plot of data for an industrial oil is shown in Figure 3.2.

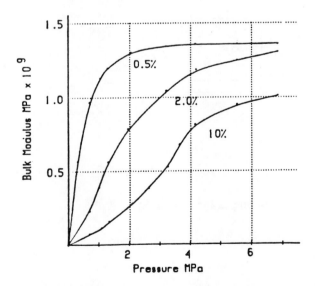

Figure 3.2 Effect of Entrained Air on Bulk Modulus

This leads to the guideline that hydraulic systems should not be designed to operate with pressures less than 7 MPa and that the free air content should not exceed 0.2% by volume.

3.2 Effective bulk modulus

The system stiffness is determined by the combined contributions of the oil, air content and structural stiffness. Since these stiffness contributions are in series, the overall value will be controlled by the weakest link in the chain, and will clearly result in a numerical value less than the oil alone. The significance of this can be seen from equation (2.24), where the response of the system is determined to a large extent by the value of the natural frequency, which in turn is determined by the value of the stiffness. So for example, the higher the percentage of entrained air in the oil, the lower the stiffness and therefore the slower the system response.

Consider an oil/air mixture being pressurized in a container. As the pressure is increased, the gas entrained in the oil is compressed (Figure 3.3), the oil itself is compressed, but the container expands a little, having a compensating effect.

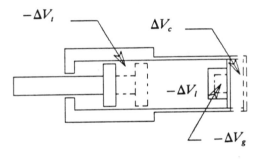

Figure 3.3 Active Bulk Modulus

The change in the total volume is then given by,

$$\delta V_t = -\delta V_g - \delta V_l + \delta V_c$$

Now since the effective bulk modulus is,

$$\frac{1}{N_e} = \frac{1}{V_t}\frac{\delta V_t}{\delta_p}$$

the same pressure increase applies to all the contributions to the overall value, therefore,

$$\frac{1}{N_e} = \frac{1}{V_t \delta p}(-\delta V_g - \delta V_l + \delta V_c)$$

$$= -\frac{\delta V_g}{V_t \delta p} - \frac{\delta V_l}{V_t \delta p} + \frac{\delta V_c}{V_t \delta p}$$

(3.8)

Applying the definition of bulk modulus to each of the contributions,

$$\frac{1}{N_g} = -\frac{\delta V_g}{V_g \delta p}; \quad \frac{1}{N_l} = -\frac{\delta V_l}{V_l \delta p}; \quad \frac{1}{N_c} = \frac{\delta V_c}{V_t \delta p}$$

Hence equation (3.8), can be rearranged as,

$$\frac{1}{N_e} = -\frac{V_g}{V_t}\frac{\delta V_g}{V_g \delta p} - \frac{V_l}{V_t}\frac{\delta V_l}{V_l \delta p} + \frac{V_c}{V_c}\frac{\delta V_c}{V_c \delta p}$$

$$= \frac{V_g}{V_t}\frac{1}{N_g} + \frac{V_l}{V_t}\frac{1}{N_l} + \frac{1}{N_c}$$

(3.9)

The gas volume is normally between 0.01% and 1% of the oil volume, although ideally 0.2% is the best practical value to aim for in a circuit.

The container could be a pipe or the cylinder of the ram. In either case, if d_1 is the inside diameter, and d_2 is the outside diameter, then for a thick-walled cylinder,

$$\frac{1}{N_c} = \frac{2}{E}\left(\frac{d_1^2 + d_2^2}{d_1^2 - d_2^2} + v\right) \tag{3.10}$$

where the Poisson's ratio v ranges from 0.25 to 0.3 for this case.
If the cylinder is thin walled or a pipe, then,

$$\frac{1}{N_c} = \frac{1}{E}\left(\frac{d_1 + d_2}{d_1 - d_2}\right)$$

$$\approx \frac{d}{tE} \tag{3.11}$$

Hydraulic hoses present a more difficult situation as they exhibit significant non-linearity with regard to bulk modulus, and there is a lot of variation in the values between the different types of hoses. Based on tests carried out on a range of hoses [7], the following imperical formula was derived,

$$N_h = 614\, d\, p_{max}^{1.5}\, (1.11 - e^{\frac{-2p}{p_{max}}})\quad \text{MPa}$$

where p_{max} (MPa) is the maximum allowable working pressure for the hose and d is the internal diameter. This formula works reasonably well up to $p = 0.5\, p_{max}$.
When assessing a value of bulk modulus for entrained gas, it is also necessary to decide on the conditions. If the temperature is constant, by allowing heat to flow into or out of the volume of gas being compressed, isothermal conditions exist and,

$$N_g = p$$

where p is the absolute pressure applied to the oil/gas mixture. If, on the other hand, heat flow is restricted, indicated by a temperature increase, then,

$$N_g = \gamma\, p \tag{3.12}$$

where γ =1.4 for air.

EXAMPLE 3.1

In an oil hydraulic press, the ram has a diameter of 20 cm and stroke is 35 cm. The piston moves in a cylinder which is supplied with oil at a pressure of 20 MPa. The total volume of oil in the connecting pipes is 4×10^{-3} m³. Before the ram can begin its return stroke, an outlet valve must open, allowing pressure in the cylinder to fall to atmosphere. Moreover, because of the compressibility of the oil, a certain volume will escape even before the ram moves. The complete circuit is shown in Figure 3.4. Note however that the relief valve does not operate in the normal functioning of this circuit, but is a safety measure. What will be the released volume, and how much elastic energy will the oil carry with it?

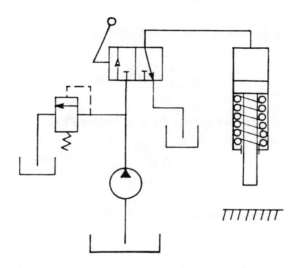

Figure 3.4 Hydraulic Press Circuit

This can be found using equation (3.4),

$$N = - V \frac{\Delta P}{\Delta V}$$

Assume rigid pipes and no aeration, the change of volume with pressure will be,

$$\Delta V = - V \frac{\Delta P}{N}$$

The swept volume for the ram is,

$$\text{Swept Volume} = \frac{\pi d^2}{4} \times L = \frac{3.14 \times (0.2)^2 \times 0.35}{4} = 0.010\ 99\ \text{m}^3$$

while the volume of oil in the pipes is given as 4×10^{-3} m^3.

Therefore total oil volume $= 1.499 \times 10^{-2}$ m^3 and will represent V in equation (3.4). The released volume is,

$$\Delta V = \frac{-1.499 \times 10^{-2} \times 20 \times 10^6}{1.38 \times 10^9} = -2.173 \times 10^{-4}\ \text{m}^3$$

The potential energy stored in a spring is given by,

$$PE = \int_0^F F\,dx = \frac{1}{2} k x^2$$

However in the case of an oil spring, the k is replaced by,

$$PE = \frac{1}{2} \frac{N}{V} A^2 x^2$$

Note that oil is only present on one side of the ram,

$$= \frac{1}{2} \times \frac{1.38 \times 10^9}{1.499 \times 10^{-2}} \times \left(\frac{\pi \times (0.2)^2}{4} \right)^2 \times \left(\frac{2.15 \times 10^{-4}}{\frac{\pi \times (0.2)^2}{4}} \right)^2$$

$$= 2.172 \times 10^3\ \text{N.m}$$

EXAMPLE 3.2

Calculate the natural frequency of the actuator-load arrangement shown in Figure 3.5. The unit consists of two pistons mounted on a rocker arm, so that the linear motion of the piston is translated into rotational motion of the drive shaft. The drive shaft is attached to the flywheel. Assume $N = 1.38$ GN/m² for hydraulic oil and the modulus of rigidity is 85 GN/m². The load inertia is 0.97 kg.m².

Experience shows that items in compression and tension offer significantly less contribution to the overall stiffness, than items in torsion. So in this case, the mechanical stiffness will be significant and should be considered with the oil stiffness as two springs in series.

The stiffness of a shaft in torsion is given by,

$$\frac{T}{\theta} = \frac{G J}{l}$$

where
T = applied torque
θ = angular deflection
G = modulus of rigidity
J = polar moment of inertia of the section
l = length of section

Referring to Figure 3.5, the contribution to torsional stiffness is the 160 mm section from the rocker arm,

$$J = \frac{3.14}{2} \times (0.0095)^4 = 1.278 \times 10^{-8} \text{ m}^4$$

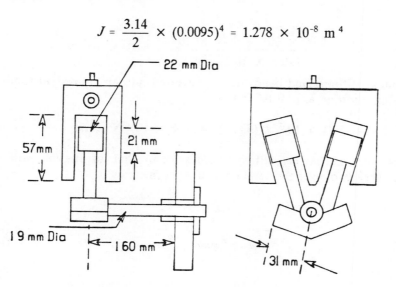

Figure 3.5 Rotary Hydraulic Actuator

Assuming the end boss holding the flywheeel is a press fit, the stiffness of the shaft will be,

$$\frac{T}{\theta} = \frac{85 \times 10^9 \times 1.278 \times 10^{-8}}{0.16} = 6.789 \times 10^3 \text{ N.m /rad}$$

The oil stiffness is calculated using the dimensions from Figure 3.5.

Volume of one piston $= 7.978 \times 10^{-6} \text{ m}^3$

Volume of one cylinder $= 2.166 \times 10^{-5} \text{ m}^3$

Swept volume of cylinder is therefore,

$$2.166 \times 10^{-5} - 7.978 \times 10^{-6} = 1.368 \times 10^{-5} \text{ m}^3$$

The oil stiffness is determined using,

$$\lambda_o = \frac{4NA^2}{V}$$

$$= \frac{4 \times 1.38 \times 10^9 \times 1.44 \times 10^{-7}}{1.368 \times 10^{-5}} = 5.81 \times 10^7 \text{ N /m}$$

This is a linear stiffness and needs to be converted into an equivalent torsional stiffness using a torque arm of 0.031 m.

$$k_o = 5.81 \times 10^7 \times (0.031)^2 = 5.58 \times 10^4 \text{ N.m/rad}$$

Notice how the mechanical stiffness is less than that of the oil stiffness. Combining these two gives the total equivalent stiffness as,

$$\frac{1}{k_{total}} = \frac{1}{k_{mech}} + \frac{1}{k_{oil}}$$

$$\frac{1}{k_{total}} = \frac{1}{6.789 \times 10^3} + \frac{1}{5.58 \times 10^4} = 1.654 \times 10^{-4}$$

$$k_{total} = 6.045 \times 10^3 \text{ N.m/rad}$$

The natural frequency is,

$$f_n = \frac{1}{2\pi}\sqrt{\frac{6.045 \times 10^3}{0.75}} = 14.3 \text{ Hz}$$

On the other hand, if we ignore the mechanical stiffness contribution, then

$$f_n = \frac{1}{2\pi}\sqrt{\frac{5.58 \times 10^4}{0.75}} = 43.43 \text{ Hz}$$

which would mislead the designer into thinking the system response was much faster than in practice.

EXAMPLE 3.3

Figure 3.6 shows the design of a press station used to apply a force of 570 kN. The single-ended, double-acting ram has a cylinder diameter of 25.4 cm and rod diameter of 17 cm. The working travel of the press for loading parts is 6.35 mm. However, there is a full travel needed from the ram of 20 cm, in order to accommodate tool and die changes.

The duty cycle requirement is,

Load and alignment of part within the 6.35 mm
working when the pumps are idle.   1.500 s

Time to move ram up to touch part after loading,   0.155 s
(distance moved to form part is assumed small).

Hold period.   1.740 s

Retract ram.   0.355 s

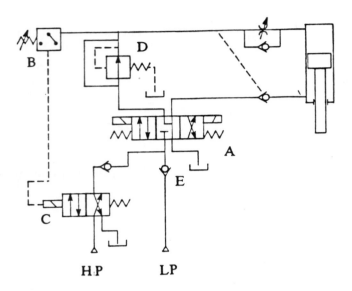

Figure 3.6   Circuit for Press Station

The duty cycle is described mainly for general information. Assume 0.03 s to build up pressure during compressibility, and to simplify the problem, assume the forming motion is small compared to the movement due to compressibility. Two pumps are used in the circuit; for the low-pressure side, 2 MPa and for the high-pressure side, 14 MPa. Efficiencies are, respectively, 80 and 85%.

The response times of the valves are given as,

Valve A	0.035 s
Valve C	0.043 s

Determine the total power requirements from the pumps.

First calculate the force requirements at the ram,

$$\text{Force} = 570,000 + (15\%) = 655,500 \text{ N}$$

Load pressure,

$$p_L = \frac{655\,500}{506.45 \times 10^{-4}} = 12.94 \text{ MPa}$$

Since only part of the cycle requires maximum force, two pumps are used:

For movement of ram requiring low pressure   2 MPa
For movement of ram requiring high pressure   14 MPa

Operation of the circuit is as follows.

Start by moving valve A to the right, which allows the ram to extend at low pressure, until pressure switch B signals valve C to shift. This now puts high pressure into the ram for the pressing operation.

Since 14 MPa > 2 MPa, the low-pressure non-return valve E is held closed. The pressure regulator (reducing) valve D is set for ≈ 13 MPa. At the end of the press cycle, the pressure switch goes off, shutting the high pressure out of the circuit, and returning control to the low pressure. Valve A is moved to the left for ram retraction.

For the operation described above, the time taken will be,

Valve A takes   0.035 s

Valve C takes   0.040 s

Total time   0.075 s

During the work cycle, the time available to extend the ram up to the part is,

Available time = 0.155 - 0.075 = 0.08 s

since some of the allotted time is used up by valve action. The ram movement during the work cycle is 6.35 mm, at which time it touches the part and pressure starts to rise,

Volume required to move 6.35 mm = $506.45 \times 10^{-4} \times 6.35 \times 10^{-3}$

$$= 0.332 \times 10^{-3} \text{ m}^3$$

Therefore required flow will be,

$$Q = \frac{0.322 \times 10^{-3}}{0.08} = 0.004 \text{ m}^3/\text{s}$$

This is the flow for the low-pressure part of the operation, hence, for the low-pressure pump,

$$\text{Power} = \frac{0.004 \times 2 \times 10^6}{0.8} = 10\,000 \text{ W}$$

$$\text{Compressed Volume} = \frac{0.01 \times V_{Total} \times p}{2000}$$

Once the ram tool fixture reaches the part, the oil pressure builds up from 2 to 12.94 MPa, which takes 0.03 s. During this part of the cycle, the fluid compressibility is estimated at 1% by volume for every 13.78 MPa. The part-forming movement is very small and can be ignored,

$$\text{Volume} = 0.01 \times (506.45 \times 10^{-4} \times 20 \times 10^{-2}) \times \frac{12.94}{13.74}$$

$$= 0.95 \times 10^{-4} \text{ m}^3$$

This corresponds to a movement of the ram of,

$$x = \frac{0.95 \times 10^{-4}}{506.45 \times 10^{-4}} = 0.001\,87 \text{ m}$$

This is extra oil volume needed to replace that used by oil compression,

$$\text{Equivalent Flow} = \frac{0.95 \times 10^{-4}}{0.03} = 0.0032 \text{ m}^3/\text{s}$$

$$\text{Power} = 0.0032 \times 13.78 \times \frac{10^6}{0.85} = 51.88 \text{ kW}$$

for the high pressure pump. Hence the total power required,

Total Power = 61.88 kW

3.3 Ram natural frequency

For a linear motion ram with equal effective piston areas, as shown in Figure 3.7, motion to the left is caused by a flow Q_1 into the ram, resulting in an exhaust flow Q_2 out of the other end. If the piston is assumed to be in the centre of its stroke, then there will be equal volumes of oil, V_1 and V_2, each side.

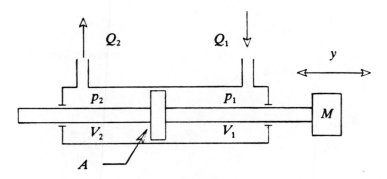

Figure 3.7 Ram Configuration

Considering side 1,

$$V_1 = \frac{m_1}{\rho_1}$$

$$Q_1 = \frac{dV_1}{dt} = \frac{1}{\rho_1}\frac{dm_1}{dt} = \frac{V_1}{\rho_1}\frac{d\rho_1}{dt} + \frac{dV_1}{dt}$$

(3.13)

It was shown in equation (3.4) that,

$$\frac{1}{N} = \frac{1}{\rho}\frac{d\rho}{dp}$$

so equation (3.11) can be rewritten as,

$$Q_1 = \frac{dV_1}{dt} + V_1 \frac{1}{\rho_1} \frac{d\rho_1}{dp_1} \frac{dp_1}{dt} = \frac{dV_1}{dt} + \frac{V_1}{N_1} \frac{dp_1}{dt}$$

Since the volume is being pressurized on side 1, it must be being released on side 2, hence,

$$Q_2 = \frac{dV_2}{dt} - \frac{V_2}{N_2} \frac{dP_2}{dt}$$

Now since the ram is symmetrical, $Q_1 = Q_2$, so the average flow, also referred to as the load flow, is given by,

$$Q_l = \frac{Q_1 + Q_2}{2} = \frac{1}{2}\left[\frac{V_1}{N_1} \frac{dp_1}{dt} - \frac{V_2}{N_2} \frac{dp_2}{dt} + 2A\frac{dy}{dt} \right] \qquad (3.14)$$

Assume that the identical oil is used each side of the piston so that $N_1 = N_2 = N$, and that the piston is at the middle of its stroke, so that $V_1 = V_2 = V/2$, where V is the swept volume. Equation (3.12) is therefore rewritten as,

$$Q_l = \frac{V}{4N} \frac{d(p_1 - p_2)}{dt} + A\frac{dy}{dt} \qquad (3.15)$$

The pressure drop across this piston, $(p_1 - p_2)$, is used to accelerate the load M,

$$p_1 - p_2 = \frac{M}{A} \frac{d^2 y}{dt^2} \qquad (3.16)$$

Combining equations (3.15) and (3.16) gives,

$$Q_l = \frac{VM}{4NA^2}\frac{d^3y}{dt^3} + \frac{dy}{dt} \qquad (3.17)$$

The stiffness of the system attributed to the oil is,

$$k_o = \frac{4NA^2}{V} \text{ N/m} \qquad (3.18)$$

and the natural frequency is,

$$f_n = \frac{1}{2\pi}\sqrt{\frac{4NA^2}{VM}} \text{ Hz} \qquad (3.19)$$

Equation (3.17) can also be written in the form,

$$Q_l = \left[\frac{1}{\omega_n^2}s^2 + 1\right]sy \qquad (3.20)$$

which, when compared with equation (2.26), shows that it represents a spring mass system with no damping. In fact, the main contribution from damping in the cylinder will come from the seals. It is therefore more realistic to rewrite equation (3.20) as,

$$Q_l = \left[\frac{1}{\omega_n^2}s^2 + \frac{2\zeta}{\omega_n}s + 1\right]sx_o \qquad (3.21)$$

The block diagram can be formulated by writing equation (3.21) with the highest derivative on the left-hand side,

$$\frac{1}{\omega_n^2}s^3y = \frac{Q_l}{A} - \frac{2\zeta}{\omega_n}s^2y - sy$$

and then the block diagram can be formed, as shown in Figure 3.8.

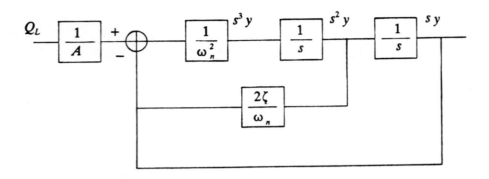

Figure 3.8 Block Diagram of Ram

EXAMPLE 3.4

A hydraulic cylinder, used to support a mass is found to have a natural frequency, $f_n = 26$ Hz, and a damping ratio $\zeta = 0.16$. If the ram piston is set in free vibrations by hitting it sharply with a hammer, which can be assumed to be simulated by a unit step to zero, determine an expression for the rod motion.

This is a spring mass damper in free vibration, therefore if y is the rod displacement, then,

$$\frac{1}{\omega_n^2} \frac{d^2y}{dt} + \frac{2\zeta}{\omega_n} \frac{dy}{dt} + y = 0$$

$$\frac{1}{\omega_n^2} = \frac{1}{(2 \times \pi \times 26)^2} = 3.75 \times 10^{-5}$$

$$\frac{2\zeta}{\omega_n} = \frac{2 \times 0.16}{2 \times \pi \times 26} = 1.96 \times 10^{-3}$$

The initial conditions are that at $t = 0$, $y(0) = 1.0$ and $v(0) = 0$. Assume that,

$$y = A e^{\alpha t}$$

is a solution, then by substitution,

$$3.75 \times 10^{-5} \alpha^2 + 1.96 \times 10^{-3} \alpha + 1 = 0$$

$$\alpha_{1,2} = \frac{-1.96 \times 10^{-3} \pm \sqrt{3.84 \times 10^{-6} - 15 \times 10^{-5}}}{7.5 \times 10^{-5}}$$

$$= -26.1 \pm 161.2 \, \text{j}$$

Since the square root is a negative number, the roots are complex and the behaviour of y will be oscillatory. The solution will be similiar to equation (2.29), hence,

$$y = e^{-26.1t} [A_1 \cos(161.2t) + B_1 \sin(161.2t)]$$

When $t = 0$, $y(0) = 1.0$, and hence,

$$A_1 = 1.0$$

When $t = 0$, $v(0) = 0$,

$$\frac{dy}{dt} = A_1(-26.1)e^{-26.1t}\cos(161.2t) + A_1 e^{-26.1t}(-161.2)\sin(161.2t)$$

$$+ B_1(-26.1)(-e^{-26.1}\sin(161.2t)) + B_1 e^{-26.1t}(161.2)\cos(161.2t)$$

or,

$$0 = A_1(-26.1) + B_1(161.2)$$

$$B_1 = \frac{-26.1}{161.2} = -0.162$$

and,

$$y = e^{-26.1t}[\cos(161.2t) - 0.162\sin(161.2t)]$$

$$= 1.013\,e^{-26.1t}\cos(161.2t - 9.54)$$

EXAMPLE 3.5

A mass of 1053 kg is supported by a ram whose stroke is 30.5 cm. The effective piston area is 19.35 x 10^{-4} m^2, and the swept volume is 58.96 x 10^{-5} m^3. Determine the natural frequency and the damping ratio, if the damping coefficient is found to be 50,000 N/m/s.

Assuming that the oil is enclosed each side of the piston,

$$f_n = \frac{1}{2\pi}\sqrt{\frac{4NA^2}{VM}}$$

$$= \frac{1}{2\pi}\sqrt{\frac{4 \times 1.4 \times 10^9 \times (19.35 \times 10^{-4})^2}{58.96 \times 10^{-5} \times 1053}} = 29.2 \text{ Hz}$$

The expression for critical damping was given in equation (2.23),

$$f_c = 2\sqrt{kM}$$

$$k = \frac{4NA^2}{V} = 35.562 \times 10^6 \text{ N/m}$$

$$f_c = 2\sqrt{35.562 \times 10^6 \times 1053} = 387\,084.07 \text{ N/m/s}$$

$$f = 50\,000, \quad \text{so that } \zeta = \frac{50\,000}{387\,084.07} = 0.13$$

EXERCISES

3.1. A mass of 500 kg is supported by a pneumatic spring, which is in the form of a single-ended ram with one end open to atmospheric pressure.

  (a) Derive an expression for the effective linear spring stiffness.

  (b) If the maximum supporting pressure is 826 kPa, what is the minimum piston area needed to support the load?

  (c) What gas volume is necessary to ensure a natural frequency of not less than 10 rad/s?

3.2. A oil-filled double-acting cylinder has a 32.5 cm stroke. The internal diameter is 80 mm, and the wall thickness is 8 mm. The Young's modulus for the cylinder material is 12×10^{10} Pa and it has a Poisson's ratio of 0.33. Compare the effective bulk modulii for thin- and thick-walled conditions.

3.3. Calculate the natural frequency of an oil-filled double-acting ram, which has a 40 cm stroke. The internal diameter is 7.5 cm and the wall thickness is 7 mm. A mass of 1250 kg is connected to the piston rod, which has a diameter of 30 mm. The pressure in the ram is maintained at 18 MPa. Assume the Young's modulus for the material as 12×10^{10} Pa, and that the oil has 0.15% air by volume.

3.4. A valve is connected to a ram by a length of hydraulic steel pipe, 1.0 m long, together with a length of flexible hydraulic hose. Both pipes have the same internal diameter of 25 mm. The steel pipe with contained oil has an effective bulk modulus of 1.4×10^9 Pa. The hydraulic hose with contained oil has an effective bulk modulus of 0.8×10^9 Pa. If the total bulk modulus of the two pipes is to be 1.2×10^9 Pa, what should be the length of the hydraulic hose?

CHAPTER 4

Leakage, friction and filters

4.1 Fundamentals

Many of the parts of fluid power components must be separated by a thin film of oil in order to ensure trouble-free operation. These gaps range in size from 2 μm up to 20 μm. There are essentially two conditions for leakage flow through such gaps:

1. A gap with no pressure gradient across it, but one wall fixed and the other moving, or both walls moving relative to each other.

2. A gap with two fixed walls and a pressure drop across it so that flow is pushed through.

In reality, most situations are a combination of both these conditions. For the first condition (Figure 4.1a), since the gap is small, the flow is controlled by the viscosity of the fluid. It can be assumed that the oil adheres to the fixed wall, taking on the velocity of the moving wall in its immediate vicinity. Hence, there is a velocity gradient proportional to the shear between the layers of fluid. Since the flow is dragged, the process acts like an inefficient pump, provided that there is no pressure at the ends of the gap, so that oil can flow freely away. The velocity profile is linear, with the maximum value occurring at the moving wall. This condition is described by Newton's Viscosity Law.

In the second case (Figure 4.1b), the fluid is driven through the gap by an external pressure difference. Both walls are fixed, so that the oil adheres to both surfaces, causing a breaking effect on the flow. The maximum flow velocity occurs in the centre and the velocity profile takes a parabolic shape.

4.1.1 Gap flow theory

Consider the classical case of two flat plates (Figure 4.2), one of which is moving at velocity v relative to the other. The plates are of width b and length l, and are separated by the distance h. The fluid between them has a viscosity μ, density ρ, and is subjected to a pressure drop.

Consider a slice of the fluid of width b, length dx and thickness dy, at a location which is a distance y from the bottom plate. Assuming laminar flow, then summing the forces in the x direction results in,

Pressure Balance + Shear Forces = 0

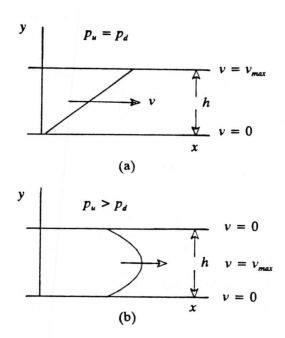

(a)

(b)

Figure 4.1a,b Laminar Flow Conditions

Since there is no acceleration, then,

$$\left[p - \left(p + \frac{\partial p}{\partial x}dx\right)\right]b.dy = \left[\left(\tau + \frac{\partial \tau}{\partial y}\right) - \tau\right]b.dx \tag{4.1}$$

giving,

$$\frac{\partial p}{\partial x} = \frac{\partial \tau}{\partial y}$$

which implies that the rate of change of pressure in the x direction must be equal to the rate of change of shear in the y direction.

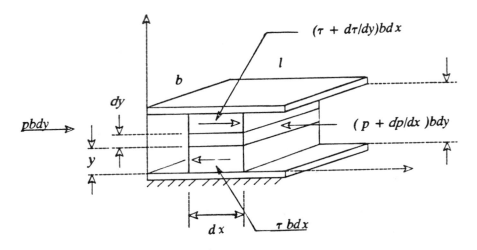

Figure 4.2 Flow Through Parallel Plates

Since $\partial p / \partial x$ is constant, then using total derivatives,

$$d\tau = \frac{dp}{dx} d\tau$$

$$\tau = \frac{dp}{dx} y + C_1$$

But from the definition of viscosity,

$$\tau = \mu \frac{dv}{dy}$$

$$\mu \frac{dv}{dy} = \frac{dp}{dx} y + C_1$$

integrating this expression,

$$\mu v = \frac{dp}{dx} \frac{y^2}{2} + C_1 y + C_2$$

The term v is the velocity value at a distance y from the fixed wall. Hence the boundary conditions are,

$$y = 0, \quad v = 0, \quad \text{and} \quad y = h, \quad v = v_{max}$$

This results in,

$$C_2 = 0$$

$$C_1 = \frac{\mu v_{max}}{h} - \frac{h}{2} \frac{dp}{dx}$$

giving the velocity at a distance y from the fixed wall as,

$$v = \frac{y v_{max}}{h} + \frac{1}{2\mu} \frac{dp}{dx} y(y - h) \tag{4.2}$$

The flow can be obtained by introducing the cross-sectional area of the gap,

$$Q = \int_0^h v.b \; dy$$

$$= b \int_0^h \left(\frac{vy}{h} + \frac{1}{2\mu} \frac{dp}{dx} y(y - h) \right) dy \tag{4.3}$$

If the flow is directed towards the right in Figure 4.1, then dp/dx is considered as negative; if it is towards the left, then dp/dx is considered as positive. Integration of equation (4.3) gives,

$$Q = \frac{bhv_{max}}{2} - \frac{bh^3}{12\mu}\frac{dp}{dx} \qquad (4.4)$$

if the former case is chosen.

The first term represents shear induced leakage, called the drag flow. Since the velocity varies linearly in this case, the term $v_{max}/2$ is the average velocity. The cross-sectional area through which the leakage passes is bd. The second term is the laminar flow due to the pressure gradient and is called the slip flow.

The plus or minus sign of the first term indicates that the moving plate can be in motion to the right or left.

For the closely fitting cylindrical element in the bore (Figure 4.3), make the substitution $b = \pi d$, hence for a stationary assembly,

$$Q_l = \frac{\pi dh^3}{12\mu}\frac{(P_u - P_d)}{l} \qquad (4.5)$$

This assumes that the insert is located exactly in the centre of the bore and that h is one half of the diametrical clearance. The diametrical clearance is usually about 0.1% of the bore diameter, and note how sensitive leakage is to the clearance. If the rod is not central, which is more likely to be the case in practice, then if there is an eccentricity offset of e, the modified equation for leakage flow is,

$$Q_l = \frac{\pi dh^3}{12\mu}\frac{(P_u - P_d)}{l}(1 + 1.5e^2) \qquad (4.6)$$

4.1.2 Associated forces

Referring to equation (4.2), then differentiating with respect to y,

$$\frac{dv}{dy} = \frac{v_{max}}{h} + \frac{1}{2\mu}\frac{dp}{dx}(2y - h)$$

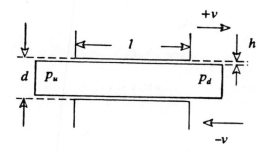

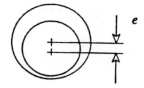

Figure 4.3   Rod Bore Leakage

Applying Newton's Viscosity Law, the shear stress will be given by,

$$\tau = \mu\frac{dv}{dy} = \mu\frac{v_{max}}{h} + \frac{1}{2}\frac{dp}{dx}(2y - h)$$

The total force acting on the moving plate will be,

$$F = \tau lb = \left(\mu\frac{v_{max}}{h} + \frac{h}{2}\frac{dp}{dx}\right) \times l \times b \qquad (4.7)$$

if dp/dx is taken as positive and $y = h$. Also if there is no pressure gradient, then the force F is that pulling the top plate at velocity v.

If both plates are fixed, then F is the force required to anchor the plates to a fixed point. In summary, if the pressure gradient is taken as positive:

(a) If the flow velocity is to the right of Figure 4.1, v is positive and,

$$Q_{total} = Q_{drag} + Q_{grd}$$

$$F_{total} = F_{grd} - F_{drag}$$

(b) If the flow velocity is to the left, v is negative and,

$$Q_{total} = Q_{grd} - Q_{drag}$$

$$F_{total} = F_{grd} + F_{drag}$$

Clearly, in the latter case, if $Q_{grd} = Q_{drag}$, there is no leakage, only a stagnation.

EXAMPLE 4.1

Figure 4.4 shows a piston partially inserted into a cylinder, and represents one piston of a piston pump. The piston diameter is 2.0 cm, and the insertion length is 50 mm. The diametrical clearance is found to be 2 x 10^{-3} cm. If the oil viscosity is 0.02 Pa.s, and the pressure is 20 MPa, determine:

1. The leakage passed the piston in the position shown.

2. The force in the y direction pushing the piston away from the cylinder wall.

Since the piston is fixed, there is no drag flow, therefore,

$$Q_l = \frac{1}{12\mu}\frac{(P_u - P_d)}{l}bh^3$$

If the piston is centrally located in the bore, the gap h will be half the diametrical clearance,

$$h = 0.5 \times 2 \times 10^{-3} \text{ cm} = 0.01 \times 10^{-3} \text{ m}$$

$$b = \pi d = 6.28 \times 10^{-2} \text{ m}$$

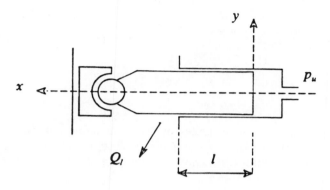

Figure 4.3 Figure for Example 4.1

$$Q_l = \frac{1}{12 \times 0.02} \times \frac{20 \times 10^6}{0.05} \times 0.0628 \times (0.01 \times 10^{-3})^3$$

$$= 10.466 \times 10^{-8} \text{ m}^3/\text{s}$$

The pressure distribution along the piston starts with a maximum value p_u, at the start of the insertion distance l and drops off linearly until $p_d = 0$ at the exit. This force is at right angles to that considered in Section 4.1.2,

$$\frac{dp}{dx} = -\frac{(p_u - p_d)}{l}$$

This pressure acts radially around the piston and tries to push it against the bore, however, since the bore is circular, the pressure must act equally in all radial directions and therefore, in theory, centralizes the piston in the bore,

$$F_y = b \int_0^l p(x) dx$$

The integral term is just the area under the pressure distribution curve, which is a triangle,

$$F_y = b \times \frac{l}{2} \times (P_u - P_d) = \frac{bl}{2} P_u$$

$$= \frac{0.0628 \times 50 \times 10^{-3}}{2} \times 20 \times 10^6 = 31,400 \text{ N}$$

EXAMPLE 4.2

A piston in a cylinder is moving under pressure, as shown in Figure 4.5. The piston length is 30 mm, and the bore diameter is 20 mm. The velocity the piston can travel at is 3 m/s in either direction. If the diametrical clearance is 60 μm, determine,

(a) The leakage flow for the piston moving to the left.

(b) If the piston now moves to the right, but the pressure distribution remains the same, what is the leakage?

The oil viscosity is 0.032 Pa.s, the upstream pressure is 20 MPa and the downstream is vented to atmosphere.
   The slip flow is determined from,

$$Q_{grd} = \frac{\pi dh^3}{12\mu} \frac{(P_u - P_d)}{l}$$

$$= \frac{1}{12 \times 0.02} \times \frac{20 \times 10^6}{0.03} \times 0.0628 \times (0.03 \times 10^{-3})^3$$

$$= 4.71 \times 10^{-6} \text{ m}^3/\text{s}$$

The drag flow is determined from,

$$Q_{drag} = \frac{\pi hd}{2} v$$

$$= \frac{3.14 \times 0.03 \times 10^{-3} \times 0.02 \times 3}{2}$$

$$= 2.83 \times 10^{-6} \text{ m}^3/\text{s}$$

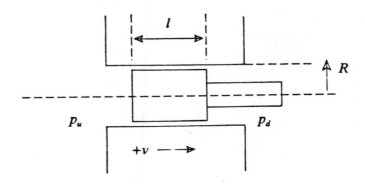

Figure 4.5 Figure for Example 4.2

If the piston is moving to the left, then,

$$Q_l = 4.71 \times 10^{-6} - 2.83 \times 10^{-6} = 1.88 \times 10^{-6} \text{ m}^3/\text{s}$$

If the piston is moving to the right, then,

$$Q_l = 4.71 \times 10^{-6} + 2.83 \times 10^{-6} = 7.54 \times 19^{-6} \text{ m}^3/\text{s}$$

EXAMPLE 4.3

A double-acting cylinder has a piston diameter of 95 mm and a diametrical clearance of 0.05 mm. No flexible seals are fitted. The piston width is 25 mm. The Young's modulus for the material used is 12 x 10¹⁰ Pa and the Poisson's ratio is 0.333. If the wall thickness is 14 mm, estimate,

(a) The leakage for a pressure drop of 18 MPa across the piston, assuming the piston is not in motion.

(b) The viscous friction coefficient.

The oil viscosity can be taken as 50 cS. Assume that $\Delta d / d = p/2N_c$

(a) Referring to equation (2.43) for a thick wall cylinder,

$$d_1 = 95 = 2 \times 14 = 123 \text{ mm}$$

$$d_2 = 95 \text{ mm}$$

$$t = 95 \text{ mm}$$

$$\frac{1}{N_c} = \frac{2}{E} \left(\frac{d_1^2 + d_2^2}{d_1^2 - d_2^2} + v \right)$$

$$= \frac{2}{12 \times 10^{10}} \left(\frac{123^2 + 95^2}{123^2 - 95^2} + 0.333 \right)$$

$$N_c = 1.39 \times 10^{10}$$

It is given that the diameter changes with applied pressure, so that when the pressure is increased from atmosphere to 18 MPa, the increase in diameter will be,

$$\Delta d = \frac{18 \times 10^6}{2 \times 139 \times 10^8} \times 95 \times 10^{-3} = 0.0615 \times 10^{-3} \text{ m}$$

Hence the radial clearance at 18 MPa is,

$$\left(\frac{0.05}{2} + \frac{0.0615}{2} \right) \times 10^{-3} = 0.0557 \times 10^{-3} \text{ m}$$

Since there is no motion, the leakage is totally due to the pressure gradient,

$$Q_{grd} = \frac{1}{12\mu} \frac{\Delta p}{l} \pi d h^3$$

$$= \frac{3.14 \times 18 \times 10^6 \times 95 \times 10^{-3}}{12 \times 50 \times 10^{-6} \times 858.2 \times 25 \times 10^{-3}} \times (0.0557 \times 10^{-3})^3$$

$$= 7.208 \times 10^{-5} \text{ m}^3/\text{s}$$

(b) The leakage coefficient is simply,

$$\frac{Q_{grd}}{\Delta p} = \frac{7.208 \times 10^{-5}}{18 \times 10^6} = 4.004 \times 10^{-12} \text{ m}^3.\text{Pa/s}$$

4.2 Hydraulic rams

The output from fluid power circuits is usually either a ram or a motor. The ram or cylinder is just a linear motor. The hydraulic motor has rotary output motion and is dealt with in detail in Chapter 6. They can be thought of as power transformers, in the sense that fluid power is applied at the input and mechanical power appears at the output. Hence they perform exactly the opposite function to pumps and compressors. Figure 4.6 shows several of the different configurations that are available, (a) is the single-acting, single-ended arrangement, where the return stroke is controlled by the mechanical spring. If the application requires both extension and retraction under power, then the double-acting equal area (b), and the double-acting, differential area (c) types are used. A less common design is the telescopic ram (d).

If it is assumed that the differential area ram (c) is in motion at constant speed against an external load F, compressibility effects can be ignored, and the force balance gives,

$$p_1 = \frac{F}{A} + \left(\frac{A-a}{A}\right)p_2$$

where a is the area of the rod cross-section, and the second term of the relationship represents the back pressure. If, on the other hand, the piston is moving in the opposite direction and the load direction is also reversed, then,

$$P_2 = \frac{F}{A-a} + \left(\frac{A}{A-a}\right)P_1$$

Hence it can be seen that it takes a larger rod end pressure to drive the load, as compared to the full area end. The piston speeds will also be different in this case. The piston moves faster when fluid is ported to the rod end than when ported to the full area end, for the same volume flow rate.

In many designs, where the loads are large, it is necessary to have a deceleration arrangement at the end of the cylinder. Once a piston is in motion, it takes on kinetic energy and at the end of its stroke, this energy has to be dissipated in order to stop the piston.

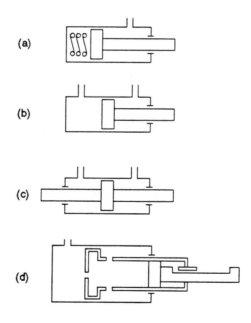

Figure 4.6 Hydraulic Ram Types

If this does not occur, then damage will be sustained to the end cap and seals. The easiest way to achieve this is with a simple shock absorber, which provides controlled deceleration at the end of the stroke. Figure 4.7 shows an annular clearance damper, but there are several other ways to control the energy absorption.

The annular clearance is half the diametrical clearance h, and the damper stroke is the length l. The kinetic energy of the load M and the moving parts of the ram are set equal to the work done during penetration of the secondary piston into the damper cavity,

$$\frac{1}{2}mv^2 = \frac{P_1}{A}l$$

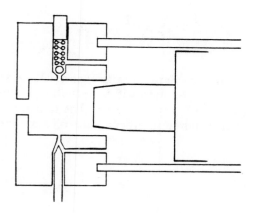

Figure 4.7 Ram Cushioning

The deceleration associated with the mass load M is,

$$\frac{dv}{dt} = \frac{P_1}{AM}$$

Assuming that the velocity falls off parabolically, then,

$$v = \frac{t}{2}\frac{dv}{dt}$$

The average pressure in the damper cavity will be,

$$p_d = \frac{4p_1}{\pi d^2 A}$$

and the differential pressure across the damper will be $p_d - p_2$, where p_2 is the back pressure, due to pushing the fluid out of the exhaust port pipe.

If the annular clearance is treated as an ordinary orifice, equation (1.19) then,

$$Q = C_d \, a \sqrt{\frac{2}{\rho}} \sqrt{p_d - p_2}$$

This relationship is derived from Bernoulli's Law and will be developed in more detail in Chapter 5. It assumes the flow will be turbulent; if the flow is assumed to be laminar then, equation (4.5) could be used. The time taken to complete the damping stroke is the time required to evacuate the oil from the damping cavity,

$$t = \frac{V}{Q}$$

and complete the damping stroke l.

A check valve is included to allow free flow to the piston on the return stroke. It is also important that the maximum pressure build-up during cushioning does not exceed the rupture pressure of the cylinder. It is also possible to control the energy dissipation further by shaping the secondary piston, and so programme, the orifice area closure. For example, a tapered spear shape is easy to machine and helps to dissipate the energy more uniformly during cushioning, whilst an inverted parabola shape, though costly, provides constant deceleration.

EXAMPLE 4.4

Suppose a piston has a velocity of 0.3 m/s, while moving a mass of 835 kg. The secondary piston, which enters the damping cavity is of length 102 mm and diameter 25.4 mm. The volume of the cavity is found to be 20.5 x 10^{-5} m^3. Assuming the area between the secondary piston and the cavity acts like an orifice, determine the annular clearance dimension, if the pressure drop is 200 kPa and the discharge coefficient is 0.62.

The force developed is,

$$F = \frac{P_1}{A} = \frac{M v^2}{2l} = \frac{835.2 \times 0.3^2}{2 \times 0.102}$$

$$= 368.47 \text{ N}$$

Now the deceleration is given by,

$$a = \frac{dv}{dt} = \frac{F}{M} = \frac{368.47}{853.2} = 0.43 \text{ m/s}^2$$

and the time it takes to empty the cavity of fluid is,

$$t = \frac{2v}{a} = \frac{2 \times 0.3}{0.43} = 1.4 \text{ s}$$

Hence the flow rate, assuming the full damping stroke is used, must be,

$$Q = \frac{20.5 \times 10^{-5}}{1.4} = 0.15 \times 10^{-3} \text{ m}^3/\text{s}$$

If this flow passes through an effective orifice area then,

$$a = \frac{Q}{C_d \sqrt{\frac{2}{\rho}} \sqrt{(P_d - P_2)}} = \frac{0.15 \times 10^{-3}}{0.62} \times \sqrt{\frac{858.2}{2}} \times \sqrt{\frac{1}{200\,000}}$$

$$= 0.112 \times 10^{-4} \text{ m}^2$$

The annular area that is used for the equivalent orifice area is,

$$a = \frac{\pi D^2}{4} - \frac{\pi d^2}{4} = \frac{\pi}{4}(D^2 - 0.0254^2) = 0.112 \times 10^{-4}$$

$$D = 0.025\,679\,3 \text{ m}$$

$$h = \frac{0.025\,679\,3 - 0.025\,400\,0}{2} = 0.000\,139\,6 \text{ m}$$

4.2.1 Seals and seal friction

There are two types of leakage conditions in fluid equipment, internal and external. A certain level of internal leakage is unavoidable, in fact it is necessary to provide lubrication for moving surfaces. Internal leakage can increase in volume as components wear or if an internal seal starts to fail. This type of leakage returns to the tank eventually. External leakage is avoidable with correct design and maintenance. It has to be avoided, as it can increase operating costs and even result in environmental pollution problems. Seals are designed to prevent leakage and maintain pressure.

The most common type of seal used for fluid power equipment is the O ring, shown in Figure 4.8, and is termed a flexible seal. It is installed in an annular groove which is a little larger than the seal diameter, so that when pressure is applied, the seal shapes itself into the area to be sealed. They are very suitable for static conditions or when movements are small. In the case of large movements, the seal tends to roll and can become damaged. Tolerancing is very important, since too much clearance can allow seals to extrude, under pressure, into the gap, causing eventual damage. Recommended values are laid down by the manufacturer. Typically, the maximum diametrical clearances between a piston and its bore would be 0.76 mm at 7 MPa down to 0.4 mm at 34 MPa.

The U ring is very effective for sealing reciprocating parts, as is the square seal. The former is illustrated in Figure 4.9, and operates on the principle that, when pressure builds up on the open side of the seal, the lips are forced apart. Hence the higher the pressure the better the seal. They will seal effectively up to around 70 MPa, but will leak a little at pressures below 3.5 MPa.

Square seals usually fall into the category of hard seals. Although there is some change of shape with applied pressure, much more reliance is placed on an interference fit, with pressure reinforcing the initial contact stresses. While it is possible to prevent any leakage under static conditions or very slow sliding conditions, there will inevitably be some leakage, where the relative movement has any appreciable velocity. Under these conditions, equation (4.4) will apply, and h will now represent the oil film thickness between the seal face and the metal surface. It can be shown [8], that the thickness of this film can be estimated from,

$$h = 0.25 \sqrt{\frac{\mu v b}{p + 2.3 p_o}}$$

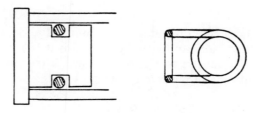

Figure 4.8 O Ring Seal

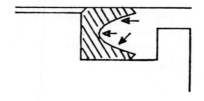

Figure 4.9 U Ring Seal

where p is the applied pressure, and p_o is the initial interference stress of the seal on the sealing surface, in the range 0.1 to 1 MPa. The oil film tends to break down if $h < 0.002\ 54$ mm. Acceptable leakage at working pressure between moving parts is around 0.2 ml/min.

A ram is a power transformer, in which fluid power enters through the input ports and mechanical power exits via the piston rod. However, account should be taken of losses in any design calculation, just as in hydraulic pumps and motors. Some of the input power will be lost as a result of seal friction. This is very difficult to calculate theoretically, and therefore we have to rely on past experience. It is generally accepted that between 10 and 15% of the stall load is a reasonable estimate, realizing that this will reduce as the piston seals wear.

EXAMPLE 4.5

A single-ended ram has a bore diameter of 63.5 mm and a rod diameter of 30 mm (Figure 4.10). The flow rate into the full area end is 0.25 x 10^{-3} m³/s. Estimate the useful output power developed while extending, if the supply pressure is 20 MPa. What is the velocity during retraction?

Full end area = 0.003 165 m²
Rod area   = 0.000 707 m²

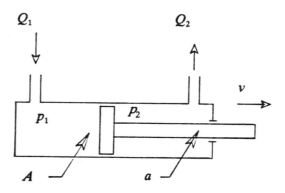

Figure 4.10 Figure for Example 4.5

Rod end area = 0.002 458 m²

It can be assumed that the valving, not shown, provides the same flow into the ram, for either direction of motion. During extension, the input power will be,

$$p \times Q = 20 \times 10^6 \times 0.25 \times 10^{-3} = 5000 \text{ W}$$

Taking into account seal friction, the force available at the rod will be,

$$F = p_1 - p_2(A - a) - 0.15 \, p_1 A$$

The back pressure p_2 is usually small enough that it can be ignored, since the return line flow is directed to the tank,

$$F = p_1 A (1 - 0.15) = 20 \times 10^6 \times 0.003\,165 \times 0.85$$

$$= 53\,803 \text{ N}$$

$$v = \frac{0.25 \times 10^{-3}}{0.003\,165} = 0.079 \text{ m/s}$$

Output Power $= 53\,803 \times 0.079 = 4250 \text{ W}$

This results in an efficiency of,

$$\frac{4250}{5000} \times 100 = 85\%$$

On retraction, the available piston area is less, but the flow is the same, so that the retraction velocity will be higher,

$$v = \frac{0.25 \times 10^{-3}}{0.002\,458} = 0.1017 \text{ m/s}$$

EXAMPLE 4.6

Calculate the required delivery pressure to each of the three circuit variations shown in Figure 4.11, just to start movement of the mass load M, which is given as 15 000 kg. In each case, the cylinder bore diameter is 9.5 cm and the rod outside diameter is 8.0 cm. As a result of back pressure, the return line pressure is 0.4 MPa. The coefficient of friction for the slideway supporting the load is 0.18.

(a) The force acting on the piston is,

Due to friction	$F_f = \mu M g$
Due to fluid pressure	$F_h = A_1 p_1 - A_2 p_2$
Due to seal friction	$F_s = 0.15 \, F_f$

Since there is only loading due to friction to overcome, and we have not started accelerating the mass, therefore,

$$A_1 P_1 - A_2 P_2 = 0.15 F_f + \mu M g = 1.15 \, \mu M g$$

$$P_1 = \frac{1.15 \mu M g}{A_1} + \frac{A_2}{A_1} p_2$$

$$= \frac{1.15 \times 0.18 \times 15\,000 \times 9.81 + 0.0021 \times 0.4 \times 10^6}{0.0071}$$

$$= 4.41 \text{ MPa}$$

(b) The only difference between (a) and (b) is that $A_1 = A_2$, hence,

$$P_1 = \frac{1.15 \times 0.18 \times 15\,000 \times 9.81 + 0.0021 \times 0.4 \times 10^6}{0.0021}$$

$$= 14.9 \text{ MPa}$$

(c) In this case F_h is different,

$$F_h = p(A_1 - A_2)$$

$$p(A_1 - A_2) = 0.15 \, F_f + \mu M g$$

$$p = \frac{1.15 \mu Mg}{A_1 - A_2} = \frac{1.15 \times 0.18 \times 15\,000 \times 9.81}{0.0071 - 0.0021}$$

$$= 6.1 \text{ MPa}$$

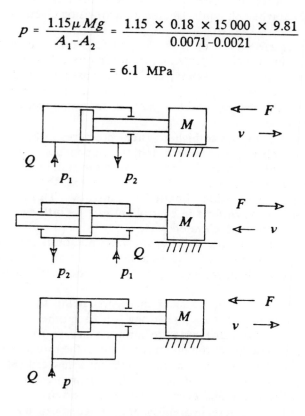

Figure 4.11 Figure for Example 4.6

4.3 Contamination control

There is little doubt that component failure or damage due to fluid contamination is an area of major concern to the designer and user of fluid power equipment.

Sources of contamination in fluid power equipment are many. For example, although oil is refined and blended under relatively clean conditions, it does accumulate small particles of debris during storage and transportation. It is not unusual for hydraulic oil circulating in a well-maintained hydraulic circuit to be cleaner than that from a newly purchased drum. In addition, after assembly of new equipment, there can still be small metal particles left over from the machining processes within the channels, despite rigorous post-production flushing.

However, clean is a relative term, so that what is clean oil for general industrial hydraulics may be too heavily contaminated for a precision electrohydraulic control system.

Finally, particles are picked up from the general working environment of the machine, through improperly maintained oil reservoirs or leaking fittings.

The contaminant level in a system can be increased internally, due to local burning of oil to create sludges. This can be a result of running the oil temperature too high (normally 40 − 50°C is recommended) or due to local cavitation in the fluid.

The trend towards the use of higher system pressures in hydraulics, generally results in narrower clearances between mating components. This is necessary to control leakage. Under such design conditions, quite small particles in the range 2−20 μm can block moving surfaces. Another problem is the wear of surfaces due to the continuous rubbing action of particles in the flow. This can be particularly damaging to square edge orifices in control valves. As little as 0.02% by weight of cement dust can cause accelerated wear.

To get a feel for the particle sizes of concern, a micron is equal to 10^{-6} m, and the human eye can just about see a 50 μm diameter particle. Hence, holding a sample of oil up to the light for examination is not the way to assess if the oil is contaminated.

To take a specific example, consider the piston pump shown in Figure 4.12. Component parts of the pump are loaded towards each other by forces generated by the pressure, and the same pressure always tends to force oil through the adjacent clearance. The life of the pump is related to the rate at which a relatively small amount of material is being worn away from a few critical surfaces. It is logical to assume, therefore, that if the fluid in a clearance is contaminated with particles, rapid degradation and eventual failure can occur.

In the case of low-pressure hydraulics, the designer can use relatively large clearances and still retain reasonable leakage control. Because the dimensions are larger, contamination is less of a problem. Hence, increasing system pressure is of major importance in determining the effect of contamination on a pump. Although the geometric clearances are fixed, the actual clearances vary with eccentricity due to load and viscosity variations.

4.3.1 Filtration

Contamination control is the job of filtration. System reliability and life are related not only to the contamination level, but also contaminant size ranges. To hold contaminant levels at a magnitude compatible with component reliability requires both the correct filter specification and suitable placement in the circuit. Correctly selected filters can be placed in the suction line, pressure line, return line or in a partial flow mode [9]. With suction line filters, the specified vacuum rating for the pump must not be exceeded. One way of providing this type of filtration without fear of cavitation is to use a magnetic separator.

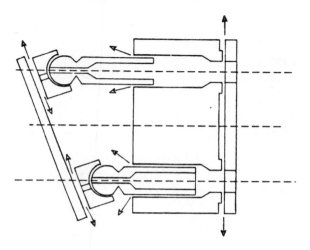

Figure 4.12 Pump Critical Clearances

Pressure line filters should be sized to withstand pressure surges as well as the system operating pressure. Various circuit configurations are shown in Figures 4.13a–e.

(a) Suction line strainers or filters must have low pressure drops, and high flow handling ability. They should be placed in the tank, with no part of the actual filter surface exposed.

(b) Delivery line filters have the advantage of total flow filtration, but there is a price to be paid in pressure loss across the filter.

(c) An alternative approach is to bleed off some of the delivery flow and dump it continuously through a filter to the tank. An orifice is included in this by-pass line to maintain constant flow. This method is more applicable to large flow systems.

(d) An independent circuit is used in this configuration, where the total oil flow is pumped through a filter, using a separate pump. This overcomes the problem of large pressure drops in the delivery line due to the filter system.

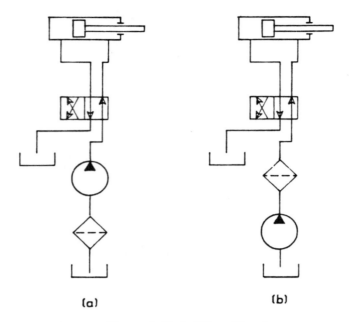

(a)   (b)

Figure 4.13a,b Filter Circuits

(e) The advantage of return line filtering is that the oil is immediately filtered
   as it returns from the working circuit. However, it is important to check that
   the back pressure created by the filter flow resistance is not excessive.

Strainers or course filters are usually of all-metal construction, and may be as
simple as a wire gauze supported on a perforated frame. Other types take the
form of a stack of metal discs held at a uniform distance from each other by
spacers, or of wire wound on a cylindrical former. Spacing between the wires is
usually around 0.13 mm, and a liberal surface area is provided to ensure as small
a pressure drop as possible, even when the filter is partially choked. These types
of filters can be back-flushed for cleaning.

Delivery line filters are constructed from a variety of materials, such as plastic
impregnated paper, stacked paper discs, felt blocks and sintered metal. In edge
or surface type elements, all the passages lie in a single surface and filtration relies
on the closeness of the pores or spacing of the material.

In depth-type filter designs, the pores have a broader size distribution and tend
to consist of long winding passages. Depth-type filters hold more debris than the
edge-type for similiar surface areas, but have higher initial pressure drop and tend
to be more bulky, since pleating of the material to increase the surface area is not

always possible. However this type of paper filter is in common use.

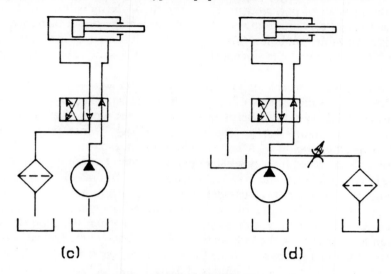

(c)   (d)

Figure 4.13c,d Filter Circuits

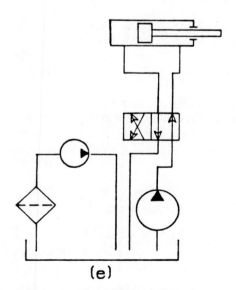

(e)

Figure 4.13e Filter Circuit

The size distribution of particles is random and, the smaller the size range, the greater the number of particles present in the fluid. Removal of particles above 100 μm is straight forward, removal of a high percentage of debris between 5 and 100 μm is achievable, but below this range is difficult and expensive. For example, a 10 μm filter is capable of removing about 98% of all particles greater than 10 μm size.

To use a gross approach of just inserting a filter with a very low rating is unsatisfactory from the aspects of cost and high pressure loss.

Dirt in hydraulic systems consists of many different types of material, ranging in size from less than 1 μm to greater than 100 μm. Most general industrial hydraulics operating below 14 MPa are able to tolerate particles up to 25 μm and therefore a 25 μm rated filter is satisfactory. Equipment operating at pressures in the 14–21 MPa range should have 20–15 μm rated filters, whilst high-pressure pumps and precision servo valves need 5 μm rated filtration.

Choosing the correct filter element requires an assessment of the sizes of clearances in the components, then determining how clean the fluid needs to be in relation to environmental conditions. Table 4.1 shows some typical component clearances. One method of classifying filters is to use a mesh size, so for example, 44 μm equals 325 mesh, 74 μm equals 200 mesh and 149 μm equals 100 mesh. Another method is the SAE classification numbers; some are shown in Table 4.2. The meaning of the classification numbers can be approximately interpreted as,

Class 2	Close tolerance system
Classes 3 and 4	Critical systems
Class 5	Medium tolerance system
Class 6	General industrial

Filter performance is measured by the extent to which silt and particulate matter can be removed from the fluid. The filter rating is a measure of the performance, and indicates that a high percentage of particles down to the filter–rated value can be removed. A more precise method is to use Beta ratings [10,11],

$$\text{Beta Ratio} = \frac{\text{Particle Count Upstream}}{\text{Particle Count Downstream}}$$

$$\text{Beta Efficiency} = \frac{\text{Particle Count (Upstream - Downstream)}}{\text{Particle Count Upstream}}$$

The ISO standard 4406 uses this rating system, and Table 4.3 shows the range number based on the number of particles larger than 5 μm and larger than 15 μm in a 1 ml sample of fluid. So for example, a fluid designated as ISO 17/14 means that there are approximately 1300 particles of 5 μm size and 160 particles of 15 μm size in a 1 ml sample of the fluid. The smaller size gives an indication of silting conditions, and the larger size relates to the potential for component wear.

4.3.2 The positive aspects of contamination

Contamination build-up in a system can be used as a diagnostic tool. Regular sampling of the oil and examination of the particles can often give a clue to potential failure of components. In other words this is a preventative maintenance tool. Many methods, for example, spectrochemical or ferrographic, can be used for this type of examination. Sampling of oil can be taken at any time and does not interfere with the operation of the equipment.

Table 4.4 shows the normally expected parts per million (ppm), levels rising above these values and particularly rates of change of levels, are indicative of potential failures.

The ferrographic technique allows the separation of wear debris and contaminants from the fluid and allows them to be arranged as a transparent substrate for examination. When wear particles are precipitated magnetically, virtually all non-magnetic debris is eliminated. The deposited particles deposit according to size and may be individually examined. By this method, it is possible to differentiate cutting wear, rubbing wear, erosion, scuffing by the size and geometry of the particles. However, the ferrographic method is expensive compared to other methods for analysis.

Table 4.1

Component	Clearance μm
Gear pump, gear tip to case	0.5–5.0
Piston pump, piston to bore	5.0–40
valve plate	0.5–5.0
Control valve, spool to sleeve	1.0–23
Servo valve, spool to sleeve	1.0–4.0
Rams, piston to bore	50–250
Hydrostatic bearings	1.0–25

Table 4.2

Range (μm)	Class number, particles/100 ml				
	2	3	4	5	6
5–10	9700	24000	32000	87000	128000
10–25	2680	5360	10700	21400	42000
25–50	380	780	1510	3130	6500
50–100	56	110	0225	430	1000
100	5	11	0021	41	92

Table 4.3

Number of particles/ml	ISO 4406 number
80000–160000	24
40000–80000	23
20000–40000	22
10000–20000	21
5000–10000	20
2500–5000	19
1300–2500	18
640–1300	17
320–640	16
160–320	15
80–160	14
40–80	13
20–40	12
10–20	11
5–10	10

EXERCISES

4.1. A mass of 2000 kg is to be accelerated horizontally from rest up to a velocity of 1 m/s over a distance of 50 mm. The coefficient of friction between the load and the guides is 0.15. Calculate the bore size for the cylinder, if the maximum allowable pressure in the cylinder is limited to 10 MPa.

4.2. Oil flow along the annular passage formed between a 10 mm diameter piston of length 20 mm and its bore. The radial clearance between the piston and rod is 0.05 mm. Calculate the leakage along the annulus, if the pressure difference is 20 MPa, and the oil viscosity is 45 cS.

4.3. A slipper pad is resting on a swash plate, and separated by an oil film of thickness 10 μm (Figure 4.12). If the oil viscosity is 20 x 10^{-3} Pa.s, and the pressure drop is 10 MPa, calculate the leakage.

Table 4.4

Material	Source in System	Max Level (ppm)
Iron	Bearings, gears, or pipe rust Pistons and valve wear	20
Chromium	Alloyed with bearing steel	4
Aluminium	Air cooler equipment	10
Copper	Bronze or brass in bearings Connectors. Oil temperature sensor bulb. Cooler core tubes	30
Lead	Usually alloyed with copper or tin Bearing cage metal.	20
Tin	Bearing cages and retainers	15
Silver	Cooling tube solder	3
Nickel	Bearing steel alloy	4
Silicon	Seals; dust and sand from pool filter or air leak	9
Sodium	Possible coolant leak into hydraulic oil	50

4.4. A slipper pad has dimensions as shown in Figure 4.14. The pressure drop is 10 MPa and the oil viscosity is 20 x 10⁻³ Pa.s. If the leakage is 0.62 x 10⁻⁶ m³/s, find the value for the separation h.

4.5. The flow rate of oil into the full area end of a 7.62 cm diameter hydraulic cylinder is 0.069 m³/min. The piston (Figure 3.15) contains a 2.54 cm diameter cushioning piston, which is 19 mm in length. This is the cylinder deceleration distance at the end of its stroke. The loading on the system is 680 kg, which slides on a flat horizontal surface, having a coefficient of friction of 0.12. The pump relief valve is set at 5 MPa, and therefore the maximum pressure at the full area end will be at this valve while the cushioning is decelerating the piston. Find the maximum pressure developed on the small area side of the piston during deceleration.

4.6. A design application requires a small cylinder to be rotated inside a fixed larger cylinder filled with oil, at 1800 rpm. The viscosity of the oil is 4 x 10⁻² Pa.s. If the maximum torque to be applied to the free cylinder is 0.97 x 10⁻⁴ N.m, find a suitable value for the separation distance h. The dimensions of the inner cylinder are diameter 1.414 cm and length 2.8 cm.

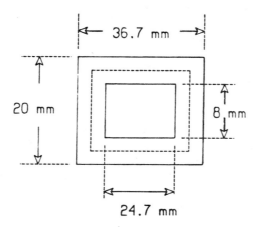

Figure 4.14 For Exercise 4.4

CHAPTER 5

Valve design and application

5.1 Introduction

The main purpose of valves in a fluid power circuit is to control output variables. Other types of valves are used in a safety role, much as fuses are used in electrical circuits.

There are two fundamental control functions for valves: directing the flow of energy in a circuit, and modifying the energy level in the fluid. The former function is the role of directional control valves, and the latter divides into two subgroups, flow and pressure control valves.

The main function of directional control is to start and stop the direction of fluid flow in a circuit by opening or closing flow passages through the valve body. In a sense, these types of valves are binary devices, in that the fluid flows through them or does not. Another type of flow control valve meters the flow over a range, and can be as simple as a manual shut-off cock, or as complex as a two stage-servo valve.

Directional control valves are classified according to:

- Number of flow paths or ports, often called ways.

- Number of spool positions.

- Methods of actuation.

The number of ways is quoted first, hence a 4/3 directional control valve means four ports connected to the pipework and three spool positions.

Symbols are a useful way of drawing and explaining the operation of fluid power circuits. They do not, however, give any performance information. There has been a significant effort made to standardize the use of symbols and most circuits are drawn to either ISO 1219 or CETOP standards. For example, Figure 5.1a shows a manually actuated directional control valve; the three possible positions are also shown.   Figure 5.1b shows solenoid and pilot actuation modes of operation.

To read drawings of this type, these symbols represent the component or circuit in its rest position, in the case of Figure 5.1a, the four pipes remain stationary and the boxes are moved to select the valve's action. Often the circuit contains a lot of components that are safety features not normally used, hence it may take some time to decide which part of the circuit is functional and which part is essentially redundant.

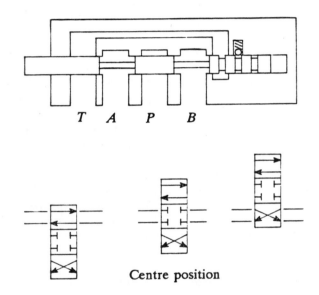

Centre position

Figure 5.1a A 4/3 Directional Control Valve

Another important feature of directional control valves is the valve centre condition. When the spool is in the central position these are:

1. Open centre (Figure 5.2a), where the ports to the cylinder must be connected to a tank in addition to the delivery line.

2. Closed centre (Figure 5.2b), all the lines to and from the valve are blocked.

3. Tandem centre (Figure 5.2c), where the cylinder lines are blocked and the delivery is directed to a tank.

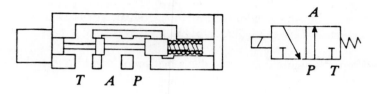

Solenoid actuated 3/2 valve

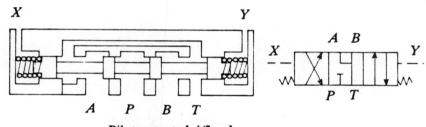

Pilot actuated 4/3 valve

Figure 5.1b Other Valve Actuation Types

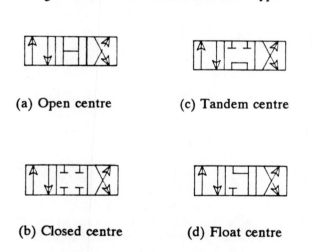

(a) Open centre   (c) Tandem centre

(b) Closed centre   (d) Float centre

Figure 5.2a–d   Directional Control Valve Configurations

4. Float centre (Figure 5.2d), where a delivery line supplies several systems,but the cylinder ports must vent to a tank with the valve central. This also allows cylinders to float or hydraulic motors to free-wheel.

5. Pressure centre (Figure 5.2e), where the valve acts as the pilot valve of a pressure-centred, pilot-operated directional control valve or is used as a regenerative connection between cylinder ports.

6. Semi-closed centre (Figure 5.2f) provides a hydraulic lock to one end of the cylinder.

7. Semi-pressure centre (Figure 5.2g), provides a hydraulic lock by blocking one port and pressurizing the other.

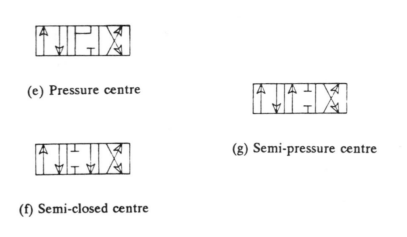

(e) Pressure centre

(g) Semi-pressure centre

(f) Semi-closed centre

Figure 5.2e–g Directional Control Valve Configurations

5.1.1 Flow control valves

While directional control valves are used to direct flow to various parts of the circuit, the flow control valve is used either to meter or block-off the flow. The non-return valve or check valve allows free flow in one direction and none in the reverse direction. Figure 5.3 shows both the simple and pilot-operated versions. The spring is usually low stiffness to hold the ball in place, and therefore only a small differential pressure is needed to hold the valve open. In the case of the pilot-operated version, a small piston can be actuated from a pilot line to keep the valve permanently open.

An example illustrating the use of non-return valves is shown in Figure 5.4. In this circuit, the direction of motion of the double-acting differential area cylinder is controlled by a pilot-operated, float centre, directional control valve. A schematic of the details of this type of valve is shown in Figure 5.1b. It can be seen that, in the rest position, the cylinder ports A and B are free to flow oil to the tank, but the delivery line from the pump is blocked at the valve, but relieves to the tank. This allows the cylinder to float, i.e. free-wheel. A further advantage is that pressure in the cylinder lines cannot build up, since both ports drain to the tank. This permits the float centre valve to be used to hold a load in any position, provided that pilot-operated non-return valves are connected as shown. When the actuator is ready to extend, the pilot line on the left-hand side non-return valve is pressurized, and the ball is pushed off its seat. Thus the oil on the rod side of the piston can exhaust to the tank.

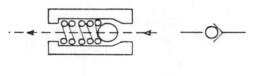

(a) Non-return valve

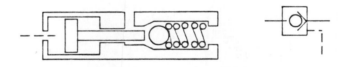

(b) Pilot-controlled non-return valve

Figure 5.3 Non-Return Valve Types

The simplest method for manual adjustable flow control is the needle valve, and this is often available with an integral non-return valve (Figure 5.5). This allows controlled flow in one direction and full flow in the opposite, a feature used in meter in and out circuits. These are a simple means of speed control. The former means that the needle valve is placed in the delivery line to a ram, restricting the flow and hence the ram speed. The latter means the needle valve is placed in the return line, which restricts the flow, but also controls any tendency for the load to run away. The needle valve gives much more precise flow adjustment than the simple shut-off valve, as it has muliple turns giving fine adjustment.

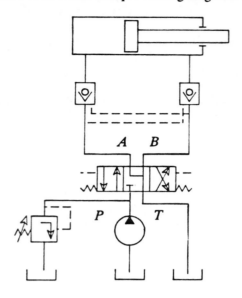

Figure 5.4 Example Circuit

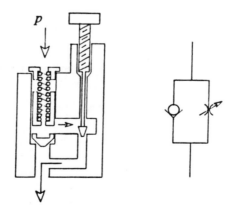

Figure 5.5 Needle Valve with Non-Return

5.1.2 Pressure relief valves

A simple form of the pressure relief valve is shown in Figure 5.6. These valves are either in shut-off mode or dumping flow to the tank, and in a sense behave like an electrical fuse, limiting the supply line pressure. Unlike the non-return valves, they are on a tee junction from the main delivery line, and not in series with the flow.

Referring to Figure 5.6, under normal circuit operation, the delivery flow $Q_p = Q_L$ and $Q_R = 0$. This means that the delivery line pressure is less than the relief pressure. When the line pressure exceeds the relief pressure then,

$$P_L \geq P_R \qquad Q_R = Q_L - Q_R$$

The relief valve orifice has a variable area, due to the spring-loaded piston, and the flow is given by,

$$Q_R = C_d A_o \sqrt{\frac{2}{\rho}} \sqrt{\delta p} \qquad (5.1)$$

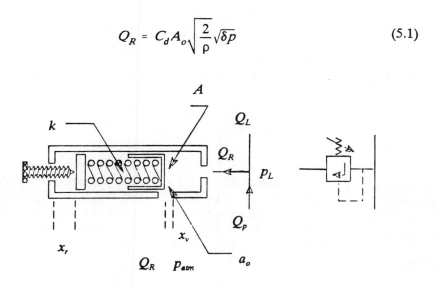

Figure 5.6 Simple Relief Valve

This is derived from Bernoulli's Law (see equation (1.20)) to be discussed in Section 5.2. The pressure drop across the relief valve, when operating, will be the relief pressure p_R, since the valve vents flow to the tank, which in turn is normally at atmospheric pressure. However, p_R also equals the minimum value of the line pressure p_L, under relief conditions.

Observation of Figure 5.6 shows that the orifice area a_o is proportional to piston displacement x, and must also be proportional to applied pressure, hence,

$$a_o \propto x_v$$

and,

$$x_v \propto (p_L - p_R)$$

where p_R is set manually,

$$p_R = \frac{x_v k}{A} \tag{5.2}$$

as long as p_L is greater than p_L.

This allows an approximate expression for the relieving pressure to be written,

$$Q_R \approx K \left(p_L - \frac{x_v k}{A} \right) \sqrt{p_L} \tag{5.3}$$

Remember that p_R is fixed manually and the delivery line pressure p_L can vary depending on the circuit loading. The dotted line in Figure 5.7 represents flow through the orifice alone, if the piston were fixed, while the solid line shows the action of the relief valve. The condition from p_R, when the valve first opens, until the relief valve is fully open at p_1, defines the opening characteristics for the valve.

5.1.3 Other valve types

Most applications cannot tolerate the wide range of cylinder speed adjustments provided by the simple needle valve, and at the same time be insensitive to load changes. To overcome this problem, the pressure-compensated flow control valve was introduced.

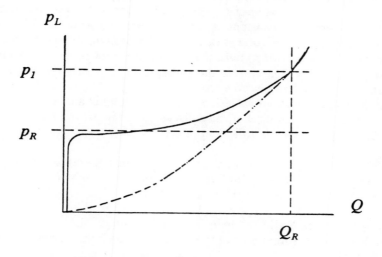

Figure 5.7 Relief Valve Characteristics

It is essentially a combination of a pressure differential valve and a variable orifice, as shown schematically in Figure 5.8.

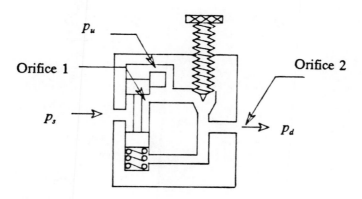

Figure 5.8 Pressure-Compensated Flow Control Valve

The spool is positioned by the pressure difference, $p_u - p_d$ across the adjustable orifice and the mechanical spring. The spool moves to the position necessary to keep this pressure drop constant at the predetermined level fixed by the spring. As the outlet pressure p_d increases, the spool moves up increasing the pressure in the control chamber. If p_d falls, the spool moves down restricting the flow Q_u and reducing p_u. By this means, the pressure drop across the needle valve is maintained constant, irrespective of load changes. In other words, the needle valve sets the flow, and the spool valve looks after any load changes.

Apart from the pressure relief valve discussed in the previous section, there are a number of other valves worth mentioning:

(a) The Unloading Valve. Like the relief valve, this operates to relieve pressure (Figure 5.9a), but the pilot line comes from a remote part of the circuit and not from the pressure upstream of the valve.

(b) The Sequence Valve. A type of pressure relief valve in which the vented fluid goes to another part of the circuit (Figure 5.9b) and is not directed to the tank.

(c) The Counterbalance Valve. Permits free flow in one direction and restricted flow in the other (Figure 5.9c). A pressurized pilot line is needed to keep the valve open.

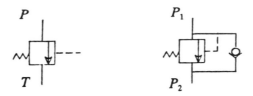

(a) Unload valve   (c) Counterbalance valve

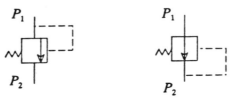

(b) Sequence valve   (d) Pressure-reducing valve

Figure 5.9a–d Pressure Control Valve Types

(d) The Pressure-Reducing Valve. Unlike the relief valve, this device is normally open (Figure 5.9d). It allows a lower delivery pressure to be set for a secondary part of the circuit.

5.2 Design of orifices

The main controlling element in any hydraulic circuit is the orifice. It is the fluid equivalent of the electrical resistance and can be fixed in size or variable, as in the case of the metering valves. The orifice is also the main source of heat generation. The pressure distribution through a fixed orifice is shown in Figure 5.10.

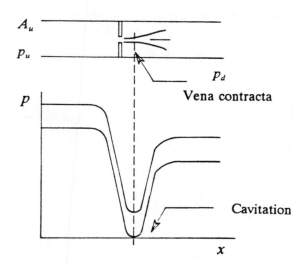

Figure 5.10 Pressure Distribution through an Orifice

The flow velocity increases as it approaches the orifice, the maximum occurring downstream of the orifice plate at the region known as the vena contracta. In this region, the local pressure is low and it is possible to create cavitation conditions. If this occurs, it can result in a significant increase in noise level and can eventually produce damage to the metal parts.

The orifice equation [12] is derived from Bernoulli's energy balance approach, so that if subscript vc is used to indicate conditions at the vena contracta, then,

$$P_u + \frac{1}{2}\rho v_u^2 = P_{vc} + \frac{1}{2}\rho v_{vc}^2 + \Delta p_f \qquad (5.4)$$

where Δp_f is the friction loss from the section upstream to the vena contracta. The continuity equation states;

$$A_u v_u = a_o v_o = a_{vc} \qquad (5.5)$$

The area at the vena contracta can be related to the orifice area using,

$$a_{vc} = C_c a_o \qquad (5.6)$$

where C_c is known as the contraction coefficient.
   Equations (5.4), (5.5) and (5.6) can then be combined to give,

$$v_{vc} = \frac{1}{\sqrt{1 - \left(\dfrac{C_c a_o}{a_u}\right)^2}} \sqrt{\left[\frac{2}{\rho}(P_u - P_{vc}) - \delta p_f\right]} \qquad (5.7)$$

By introducing a velocity coefficient, defined by,

$$c_v = \sqrt{1 - \frac{\delta p_f}{P_u - P_{vc}}} \qquad (5.8)$$

and since,

$$Q = a_{vc} v_{vc} = C_c a_o v_{vc} \qquad (5.9)$$

the flow rate can be expressed as,

$$Q = \frac{C_c C_v a_o}{\sqrt{1 - \left(\dfrac{C_c a_o}{a_u}\right)^2}} \sqrt{\frac{2}{\rho}(p_u - p_{vc})} \tag{5.10}$$

Since A_u is much larger then a_o, and since it is more convenient to talk in terms of p_d, rather than p_{vc}, the practical form of equation (5.10) is,

$$Q = c_d\, a_o \sqrt{\frac{2}{\rho}}\, \sqrt{p_u - p_d} \tag{5.11}$$

$$= 3.12 \times 10^{-2}\, a_o \sqrt{p_u - p_d}\ \ \text{m}^3/\text{s}$$

where a_o has units of m² and p has units of Pa.

In the case of an orifice of variable area, the uncovered area can be calculated from,

$$a_o = (\theta - \sin\theta)\, r^2/2 \tag{5.12}$$

here $\qquad\qquad \theta = 2 \cos^{-1}(r - x)/r$

The area displacement characteristic is plotted in Figure 5.11, which illustrates the non-linear nature of the curve.

One of the significant differences between the theoretical valve and the practical valve is the lap. Referring to Figure 5.12, the spool is the moving part of the valve, which consists of a centre rod with several piston-like parts called lands. The fixed part of the valve is called the sleeve. When the spool is in its centre position, if the lands exactly cover the flow control orifices, then the valve would be said to be zero lapped. It is not economical to produce zero-lapped valves, and therefore normally valves are either overlapped or underlapped.

An overlapped valve saves fluid loss when the spool is central, which is good for directional valves, in the sense that it provides a hydraulic lock on any ram or motor connected to the valve. However, if the valve is a precision servo type there can be both accuracy and stability problems, especially in a closed-loop configuration.

An underlapped valve gives much better control and stability at the cost of a higher leakage rate. There is also a loss of the hydraulic lock characteristic, so that reverse loading on a ram or motor cannot be handled satisfactorily without reverting to a control loop.

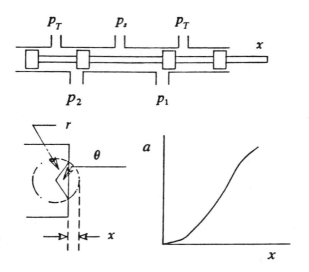

Figure 5.11 Effective Orifice Area

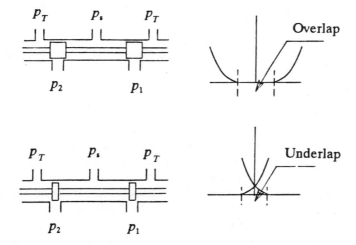

Figure 5.12 Valve Lap Types

5.2.1 Valve design

From a practical point of view, a spool valve should have at least three orifices distributed around the perimeter of the sleeve, simply to ensure an even distribution of pressure around the spool lands. This keeps the spool centralized and floating on an oil film. In small spools, it may be necessary to have only two orifices to ensure a low enough hydraulic gain, meaning the ratio of flow out to a unit valve displacement. One orifice can never be used, since the spool would jam in the sleeve. Even with these precautions, if left under pressure, the spool will still move to some favoured position, towards the inner surface of the sleeve. This is simply because it is not practical to machine the spool to be perfectly concentric with the sleeve. When pushed in the favoured direction by the pressure gradient and on reaching the wall, the spool land can break through the oil film to cause metal-to-metal contact. This is called hydraulic stiction and the valve is essentially seized until the supply pressure is turned off.

An alternative design is the annular orifice. This has a much more linear characteristic, but can result in a problem of high valve gain, especially with small spools.

Figure 5.13 shows the detailed construction of typical spool valves. The design relationship for flow through either type valve was shown earlier in equation (5.11). The uncovered orifice area can be determined from equation (5.12) for the circular orifice. If an annular orifice is used, the uncovered area calculation is simplified to,

$$a_o = 2\pi r x_v \qquad (5.13)$$

This flow equation is a function of two variables, which is difficult to handle in design calculations. One approach is to linearize the equation and consider small movements about a selected operating position, usually the centre position.

5.3 Valve performance

Examination of equation (5.11) shows that it is a function of two variables, pressure drop and uncovered orifice area. This means that there are many combinations of pressure drop and valve position that will produce the same flow out of the valve when it is in a circuit.

To attempt to overcome this problem, a linearization process can be applied, which is valid provided that only small movements of the system about some reference position are considered. First we will review the mathematics of this approach, since it is very useful for any non-linear relationship, then apply the method to the particular situation of a valve.

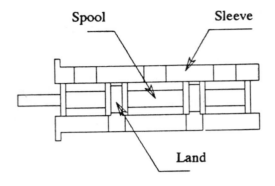

Figure 5.13 Typical Spool Valve Design

5.3.1 Single variable case

This approach can be applied to any non-linear relationship, provided that the region of interest is confined to small movements or perturbations about a steady-state condition. This condition can however be selected anywhere on the curve, and is called the operating point. For example, consider the curve shown in Figure 5.14, which is for some relationship where $y = f(x)$, and is not directly related. The operating point is selected at x_r, y_r. Apply Taylor's formula to the curve equation, giving,

$$y = f(x_r) + \frac{d}{dx} f(x - x_r) + \frac{1}{2!} \frac{d^2}{dx^2} f(x - x_r)^2 + \dots$$

where the derivatives are evaluated at $x = x_r$.

If $(x - x_r)$ is small, then ignore the higher terms, so that,

$$y = f(x_r) + \frac{d}{dx} f(x - x_r) = y_r + K(x - x_r)$$

$$y - y_r = K(x - x_r)$$

$$\Delta y = K \Delta x$$

here K is the slope of the curve at the operating point. In other words, the curve is approximated to a straight line around the operating point.

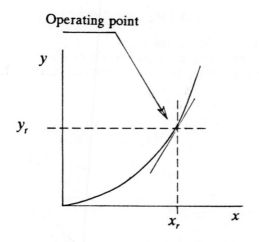

Figure 5.14 Single Variable Case

5.3.2 Double variable case

Now write an equation that is a function of two variables, and apply Taylor's formula in a similar way as it was used for the single variable case,

$$y = f(x_1, x_2)$$

$$= f(x_{r1}, x_{r2}) + \left[\frac{\partial}{\partial x_1}(x_1 - x_{r1}) + \frac{\partial}{\partial x_2}(x_2 - x_{r2}) \right] + \ldots$$

Again higher order terms are ignored, however there are two slopes to evaluate at the operating point, $x_1 = x_{r1}$, and $x = x_{r2}$,

$$(y - y_r) = K_1(x_1 - x_{r1}) + K_2(x_2 - x_{r2})$$

$$\Delta y = K_1 \Delta x_1 + K_2 \Delta x_2$$

This is shown in Figure 5.15. Equation(5.11)can therefore be written as,

$$Q = f(x_v [p_1 - p_2])$$

which refers to flow through one side of the valve.

Let ΔQ and Δx_v be small movements (relative to the orifice diameter) about a selected position; then, since $p_1 (= p_s)$ is usually constant, and applying Taylor's formula,

$$Q = Q_{ref} + \frac{\partial Q}{\partial x_v} \Delta x_v + \frac{\partial Q}{\partial (p_1 - p_2)} \Delta(p_1 - p_2)$$

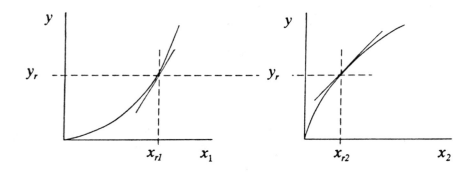

Figure 5.15 Two Variable Case

Ignoring the higher derivative terms,

$$Q - Q_{ref} = \frac{\partial Q}{\partial x_v} \Delta x_v + \frac{\partial Q}{\partial (p_1 - p_2)} \Delta(p_1 - p_2) \tag{5.14}$$

where Δx_v and $\Delta(p_1 - p_2)$ are small perturbations from the operating point Q_{ref}, as seen in Figure 5.16.

Equation (5.14) says that the linearized flow is made up of a contribution as a result of the valve spool being displaced, and a contribution due to the change in pressure.

The slope of the $Q - v - x_v$ curve is called the flow gain, or C_{xv} for the valve.

The slope of the $Q - v - (p_1 - p_2)$ curve is called the pressure gain, or C_{pg} for the valve.

The valve modulus is given by,

$$\frac{\partial (p_1 - p_2)}{\partial x_v} = \frac{C_{xv}}{C_{pg}}$$

The slope of the flow/pressure curve can be interpreted in two ways, either as the tangent conductance, which is the tangent slope about an operating point,

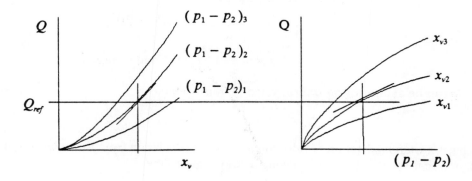

Figure 5.16   Linearized Valve Characteristics

$$G_{tg} = \frac{\Delta Q}{\Delta(p_1 - p_2)}$$

or as the secant conductance, which is taken as a straight line from the origin, Figure 5.17.

$$G_{sec} = \frac{Q}{(P_1 - P_2)}$$

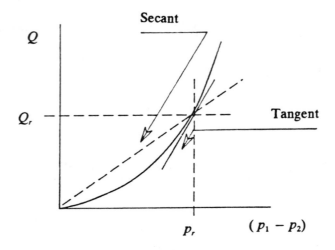

Figure 5.17 Tangent and Secant Conductance

It can be shown for an orifice, when $Q \propto p^{0.5}$, then,

$$G_{tg} = 0.5 \ G_{sec}$$

This is a useful indication of valve linearity, as any deviation from this relationship shows that the valve is not behaving as true orifice flow.

5.4 Valve ram combination

5.4.1 The four-way valve

For the combination shown in Figure 5.18,

$$Q_1 = c_d \ \sqrt{2/\rho} \ a \sqrt{P_s - P_1}$$

$$Q_2 = c_d \ \sqrt{2/\rho} \ a \sqrt{P_2 - P_E}$$

(5.15)

If the valve is symmetrical and there is no cavitation, $Q_1 = Q_2$, and therefore, $P_s - P_1 = P_2 - P_E = P_2$ since p_E is at atmosphere. Then,

$$Q_L = \frac{1}{2}(Q_1 + Q_2) = (c_d/2)\sqrt{2/\rho}\ a(\sqrt{P_s - P_1} + \sqrt{P_2})$$

$$= (c_d/2)\sqrt{2/\rho}\ a(2\sqrt{P_s - P_1})$$

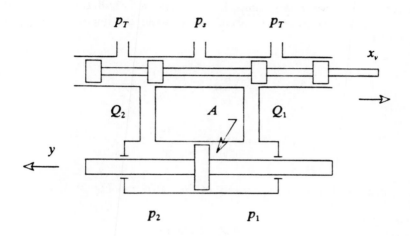

Figure 5.18 Valve Ram Combination

Now since

$$P_s = P_1 + P_2 \qquad \text{and if} \qquad P_L = P_1 - P_2$$

then,

$$P_s + P_L = P_1 + P_2 + (P_1 - P_2) = 2p_1$$

or,

$$p_1 = (p_s + p_L)/2$$

Hence,

$$Q_L = (c_d/2) \sqrt{2/\rho} \ a \ 2 \ \sqrt{P_s - \frac{P_s + P_L}{2}} \tag{5.16}$$

$$= c_d \left(a/\sqrt{\rho} \right) \sqrt{P_s - P_L}$$

Since p_s is constant, the characteristics can be expressed as shown in Figure 5.19. This is the exact valve relationship; however, there is still the problem of the equation being a function of two variables. Applying the linearization process to equation (5.15),

$$\Delta Q_1 = \left(\frac{\partial Q_1}{\partial x_v} \right) \Delta x_v + \left(-\frac{\partial Q_1}{\partial p_1} \right) \Delta p_1$$

$$\Delta Q_2 = \left(\frac{\partial Q_2}{\partial x_v} \right) \Delta x_v + \left(\frac{\partial Q_2}{\partial p_2} \right) \Delta p_2$$

However, it is clear from the symmetry of the valve and Figure 5.20 that,

$$\frac{\partial Q_1}{\partial x_v} = \frac{\partial Q_2}{\partial x_v}$$

$$-\frac{\partial Q_1}{\partial p_1} = \frac{\partial Q_2}{\partial p_2}$$

Collecting terms,

$$\Delta Q_L = \left(\frac{\Delta Q_1 + \Delta Q_2}{2} \right)$$

$$= \frac{1}{2} \left(2\frac{\partial Q_1}{\partial x_v} \right) \Delta x_v + \frac{1}{2} \left(-\frac{\partial Q_1}{\partial p_1} \Delta p_1 + \frac{\partial Q_2}{\partial p_2} \Delta p_2 \right)$$

$$= \frac{\partial Q}{\partial x_v} \Delta x_v - \frac{1}{2} \frac{\partial Q}{\partial P_1}(\Delta P_1 - \Delta P_2)$$

$$= C_{xv} \Delta x - \frac{1}{2} C_{pg} \Delta P_L \tag{5.17}$$

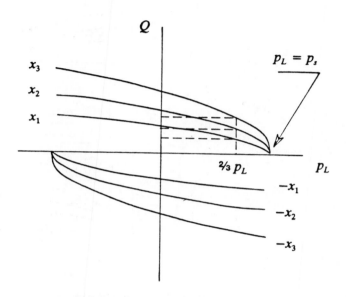

Figure 5.19 Pressure Flow Characteristics

5.4.2 Connecting the valve to a loaded ram

The combination of a four-way valve and a linear actuator is shown in Figure 5.18. The loading on the ram is shown as mass, since this is the worst design case, because of the acceleration and deceleration involved. A lot of kinetic energy can be built up, which has to be dissipated, and the compressibility of the fluid becomes important. The actuator equation was discussed in Chapter 3, where it was shown in equation (3.17), that for small movements,

$$Q_L = A \left(\frac{dy}{dt} + \frac{VM}{4NA^2} \frac{d^3y}{dt^3} \right)$$

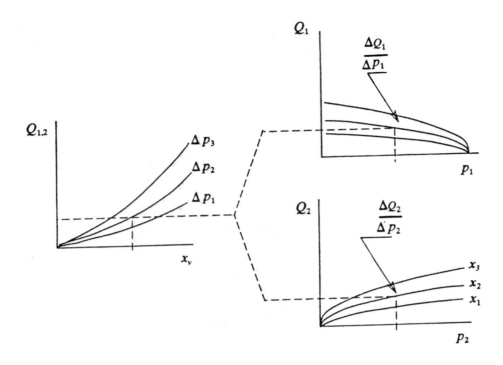

Figure 5.20 Valve Ram Characteristics

It was shown in equation (5.15) that the exact equation for the four-way valve is,

$$Q_L = C_d \frac{a}{\sqrt{\rho}} \sqrt{P_s - P_L}$$

Since the load is solely mass, the load pressure can be expressed in terms of the output acceleration,

$$P_L = \frac{F}{A} = \frac{M}{A} \frac{d^2 y}{dt^2}$$

Hence, combining these equations results in the exact valve actuator equation, which can be seen to be non-linear with no exact solution,

$$a \frac{C_d}{\sqrt{\rho}} \sqrt{P_s - \frac{M}{A} \frac{d^2 y}{dt^2}} = A \left(\frac{dy}{dt} + \frac{VM}{4NA^2} \frac{d^3 y}{dt^3} \right) \tag{5.18}$$

However, an approximate solution can be obtained using a binomial expansion [13], and ignoring higher order terms,

$$K x_v \left(1 - \frac{M}{2A p_s} \frac{d^2 y}{dt^2} \right) = A \left(\frac{dy}{dt} + \frac{1}{\omega_n^2} \frac{d^3 y}{dt^3} \right) \tag{5.19}$$

where,

$$a \approx K_v x_v$$

$$K = K_V C_d \sqrt{\frac{P_s}{\rho}}$$

therefore,

$$K x_v = \frac{1}{\omega_n^2} \frac{d^3 y}{dt^3} + \frac{KM}{2A p_s} x_v \frac{d^2 y}{dt^2} + A \frac{dy}{dt} \tag{5.20}$$

Comparing equation (5.20) with the general equation for a spring mass damper, equation (2.26), we see that,

$$\frac{2\zeta}{\omega_n} = \left(\frac{KM}{2A p_s} \right) x_v$$

$$\zeta = \left(\frac{KM \omega_n}{4A p_s} \right) x_v$$

Notice how the damping ratio is a function of the valve displacement, illustrating the non-linear nature of this component.

Another solution can be obtained using the linearized approach, where equation (3.17) is set equal to equation (5.17), so that,

$$C_{xv} \Delta x_v - \frac{1}{2} C_{pg} \Delta p_L = A\left(\frac{dy}{dt} + \frac{VM}{4NA^2}\frac{d^3y}{dt^3}\right) \qquad (5.21)$$

If the load is very small, the compressibility effect can be ignored, and equation (5.21) reduces to,

$$C_{xv} \Delta x_v = A\frac{dy}{dt}$$

$$y = \frac{C_{xv}}{A}\int \Delta x_v\, dt \qquad (5.22)$$

This shows that a lightly loaded valve actuator combination behaves as an integrator.

5.5 Optimum operational conditions

A reasonable optimization criterion would be to maximize the power output to the load,

$$\text{Output power} = P_L \times Q_L$$

$$= P_L \times C_d \frac{a}{\sqrt{\rho}} \sqrt{P_s - P_L}$$

Differentiate power with respect to load pressure,

$$\frac{d\,(\text{power})}{dp_L} = C_d \frac{a}{\sqrt{\rho}}\left(\sqrt{P_s - P_L} - P_L \times \frac{1}{2} \times \frac{1}{\sqrt{P_s - P_L}}\right)$$

For maximum power, set the left-hand side of the equation to zero,

$$\sqrt{P_s - P_L} = \frac{P_L}{2\sqrt{P_s - P_L}}$$

giving,

$$P_L = \frac{2}{3}P_s \tag{5.23}$$

Referring to Figure 5.19, this condition defines rectangles of maximum area under the flow–load pressure curves for each valve displacement.

Usual design practice is to establish the maximum actuator load including friction, then determine a piston area based on the above criterion. The remaining part of the supply pressure is then available for designing the valve. Generally, single-stage valves are available up to around 7.5 kW power handling capacity; above that value, the flow forces become too high (see Section 5.6). For higher power handling capacity, two-stage valves are available.

EXAMPLE 5.1

A hydraulic unit, similar to that shown in Figure 5.18, consists of a four-way control valve and a ram. Each set of control orifices, used to meter the flow in and out of the ram, has an uncovered area gain of 2.05 mm^2/m of valve displacement. If the oil supply pressure is 13.78 MPa, and the ram is working into a constant force of 3558.4 N, with a constant velocity of 61.75 cm/s, determine:

(a) The pressure drop per control orifice set for maximum power tansmission to the load.

(b) The required effective piston area for the ram.

(c) The diameter of each control orifice for these working conditions.

(a) The supply pressure is 13.78 MPa, so 1/3 should be dropped across the valve and 2/3 used to provide the force. The valve pressure drop provides the velocity at the output of the ram,

$$p = 1/2(1/3 \times 13.78) = 2.296 \text{ MPa}$$

Note the 1/3 is dropped across the valve, so half of that must be dropped across each orifice set.

(b) The pressure available to overcome the load is,

$$p_L = 2/3 \ p_s = 9.186 \text{ MPa}$$

so the effective piston area is therefore,

$$A = \frac{\text{load} + \text{seal friction}}{p_L}$$

$$= \frac{3558.4 + 0.15 \times 13.78 \times 10^6 \times A}{9.186 \times 10^6}$$

where the seal friction is taken as 15% of the stall force,

$$9.186 \times 10^6 \times A = 3558.4 + 2.068 \times 10^6 \times A$$

$$A = 4.99 \times 10^{-4} \text{ m}^2$$

(c) For a fluid metering valve,

$$Q = vA = 0.6175 \times 4.99 \times 10^{-4} = 3.08 \times 10^{-4}$$

$$Q = 3.12 \times 10^{-2} a\sqrt{p_u - p_d} \quad \text{m}^3/\text{s}$$

For the total orifice area, each side of the valve will be,

$$a = \frac{3.08 \times 10^{-4}}{3.12 \times 10^{-2} \times \sqrt{2.296 \times 10^6}} = 6.51 \times 10^{-6} \text{ m}^2$$

Assuming a minimum of three orifices per set, and an opening of not more than 50% to provide the required area,

$$\pi \frac{d^2}{4} = 2 \times \frac{1}{3} \times 3.357 \times 10^{-6}$$

$$d = 2.35 \times 10^{-3} \text{ m}$$

5.6 Forces associated with valves

Many of the applications require electrical signals to control valves. The driving devices can be solenoids, or some form of electric motor. It is desirable that the forces required to move a spool valve be small, linear in nature and as independent of output loading as possible. The forces to be overcome are:

1. Friction between the spool and the sleeve, which should be due to a lubricating oil film.

2. Steady-state hydrodynamic forces.

3. Transient hydrodynamic forces.

4. Force required to accelerate the spool mass and its attachments.

Apart from the basic friction forces due to oil film shear, a phenomenon termed stiction can occur if the valve has been sitting idle for a long period. This is a result of lack of symmetry between the spool and the sleeve, due to the manufacturing process. The uneven distribution of pressure results in the spool being gradually pushed towards a favoured wall. Perfect machining is not practical and various techniques of grooving the lands have been employed with success. Another approach is the use of a high-frequency driving signal, to be directed to the valve through the torque motor. This dither keeps the valve in a low-amplitude vibrating mode, whilst the imposed frequency is too high to pass through to the ram.

After static force balancing has been achieved and stiction effects minimized, a further force arises due to the change in momentum of the fluid as it passes through the valve orifices. This steady-state flow force or Bernoulli force can be seen in Figure 5.21. As the flow enters the valve through the supply pressure port, it enters a relatively large chamber, so velocity is low and local pressure high. As it leaves this chamber, it passes through the small uncovered area of the control orifices, so the local pressure now becomes low, since the velocity of the flow through the small orifice area is high. The pressure difference across the chamber walls results in a force which tries to close the valve.

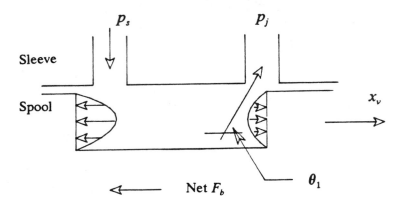

Figure 5.21 Flow Forces

It can be shown that [13],

$$F_B = 2\, C_d\, a\, \Delta p \cos \theta_1 \qquad \text{per orifice set} \qquad (5.24)$$

It can also be shown from experiment that the jet flow from the orifice is normally at an angle of 69°. Note also that this force is dependent on the square root of the pressure drop across the valve, which in turn is dependent on the output loading conditions at any particular instant.

This problem can be reduced by shaping the spool and sleeve [14], as shown in Figure 5.22.

Since there is a force developed at each end of the spool (Figure 5.21), reduction could be achieved if one of the force components could have its direction changed by 180°. Hence, spool shaping is a process of force cancellation, so that if $\theta_2 < \theta_1$, the force will tend to open the valve rather than close it.

$$F_B = \rho\, Q v (\cos\theta_1 - \cos\theta_2)$$ (5.25)

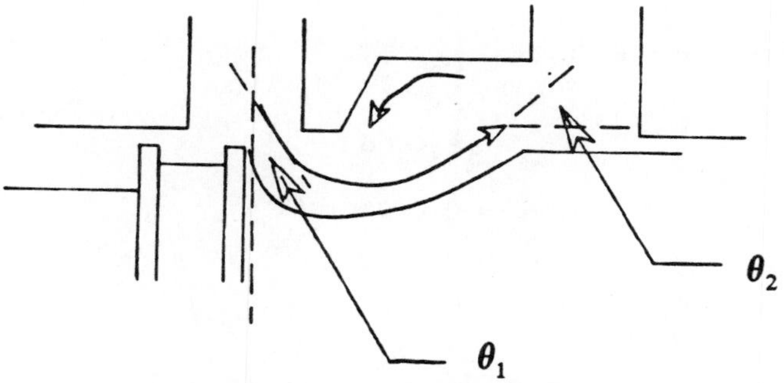

Figure 5.22 Flow Force Compensation

The primary purpose of reducing the flow force is to reduce the force into which the electromechanical driver must work, which can also be thought of as reducing a non-linear spring. If the flow force is successfully reduced, then the drive motor is often externally loaded with a linear mechanical spring, allowing the hydraulic gain to be adjustable.

EXAMPLE 5.2

A single stage-valve has a spool mass of 0.5 kg and a diameter of 19 mm. The spool is centralized by springs of total stiffness 3500 N/m. If the supply pressure is 0.7 MPa, determine the natural frequency of the assembly, with and without the hydraulic pressure present. Assuming annular control orifices, what force is needed to move the spool, for a flow of 0.98×10^{-3} m^3/s?

(a) Without hydraulic pressure there are no flow forces present,

$$f_n = \frac{1}{2\pi}\sqrt{\frac{k}{m}}$$

$$= \frac{1}{2\pi}\sqrt{\frac{3500}{0.5}} = 13.9 \text{ Hz}$$

(b) With pressure present, the flow force acting on the total valve,

$$F_B = 2 \times (2\, C_d\, a\, \Delta p \cos \theta)$$

Since the orifices are annular,

$$a = \pi\, d\, x$$

$$C_d = 0.65, \quad \theta = 69°$$

giving the effective flow force spring as,

$$\frac{F_B}{x} = 0.9318 \times \pi \times d \times \Delta p$$

$$= 0.9318 \times 3.14 \times 0.019 \times 0.7 \times 10^6$$

$$= 38\,913.8 \ \text{N/m}$$

showing that the effect of the flow force spring is much greater. These two springs act in parallel, because if we were to remove the mechanical spring, the assembly would still work,

$$\text{Total stiffness} = 38\,913.8 + 3500 = 42\,413.8 \ \text{N/m}$$

Modified natural frequency,

$$f_n = \frac{1}{2\pi} \sqrt{\frac{42\,413.8}{0.5}} = 46.38 \ \text{Hz}$$

(c) Using equation (5.11) to determine the flow,

$$Q = 3.12 \times 10^{-2} \times \pi\, d\, x \times \sqrt{0.7 \times 10^6}$$

$$0.93 \times 10^{-3} = 3.12 \times 10^{-2} \times 3.14 \times 0.019 \times \sqrt{0.7 \times 10^6} \times x$$

$$x = 0.597 \text{ mm}$$

therefore,

$$F_B = 38\,913.8 \times 0.000\,597 = 23.23 \text{ N}$$

5.6.1 Valve stability

During unsteady or transient conditions, the flow rate is not steady and the fluid acceleration gives rise to force in addition to the flow force discussed in the previous section.

It can be shown [15] that the net transient force is given by,

$$F_{tr} = \rho \, (L_1 - L_2) \, \frac{dQ}{dt} \tag{5.26}$$

where $L_1 - L_2$ is called the damping length (Figure 5.23).

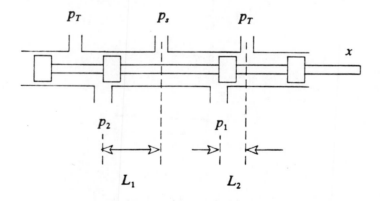

Figure 5.23 Valve Damping Length

It is found that, if $L_1 < L_2$, the damping length is negative and the spool tends to be unstable. This can cause a high-frequency oscillation termed valve sing.

5.7 Pneumatic valves

Valves using gas as the operating fluid may look the same from a mechanical construction point of view, but have several quite different performance characteristics. For example, gas density and volume are sensitive to changes in pressure, so mass rather than volume flow rate is generally used. There is the phenomenon of choked flow, which does not occur with valves controlling liquids. Gas flow does not cause cavitation, but liquid flow does.

Apply the Conservation of Energy to the valve configuration shown in Figure 5.24,

$$C_p \left(T_u - T_d \right) = \frac{v_d^2 - v_u^2}{2} \tag{5.27}$$

since $v_u << v_d$, so from equation (5.27),

$$V_d = \sqrt{2C_p \left(T_u - T_d \right)} \tag{5.28}$$

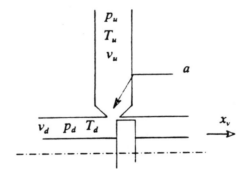

Figure 5.24 Pneumatic Valve Port

Compare this with the equivalent equation (5.11) for oil,

$$v = C_d \sqrt{\frac{2}{\rho}} \sqrt{p_u - p_d}$$

C_p and $T_u - T_d$ are not convenient physical characteristics to measure, but T_u and p_u are, so using,

$$T_d = T_u \left(\frac{p_d}{p_u}\right)^{\frac{\gamma-1}{\gamma}} \quad \text{where} \quad \gamma = C_p / C_v$$

and assuming an adiabatic process,

$$v_d = \sqrt{2 C_p T_u \left(1 - \left[\frac{p_d}{p_u}\right]^{\frac{\gamma-1}{\gamma}}\right)} \tag{5.29}$$

and,

$$W_t = \rho_t a v_d \tag{5.30}$$

where
$$\rho_t - \text{kg/m}^3$$
$$a \ - \text{m}^2$$
$$v_d \ - \text{m/s}$$

$$\rho_t = \rho_u \left(\frac{p_d}{p_u}\right)^{1/\gamma} \tag{5.31}$$

Substitute (5.30) and (5.31) in (5.29),

$$W = \rho_u a \left(\frac{p_d}{p_u}\right)^{1/\gamma} \sqrt{2 C_p T_u \left(1 - \left[\frac{p_d}{p_u}\right]^{\frac{\gamma-1}{\gamma}}\right)} \tag{5.32}$$

For a perfect gas,

$$\rho_u = \frac{P_u}{RT_n} \qquad \text{and} \qquad C_p = \frac{\gamma R}{\gamma - 1} \tag{5.33}$$

and equation (5.32) becomes,

$$W = a \sqrt{\frac{2\gamma}{R(\gamma - 1)}} \frac{P_u}{\sqrt{T_u}} \left(\frac{P_d}{P_u}\right)^{1/\gamma} \sqrt{1 - \left(\frac{P_d}{P_u}\right)^{\frac{\gamma - 1}{\gamma}}}$$

However, experimental data will show that:

(a) $C_d = 0.8$.

(b)   Choked flow occurs at $p_u/p_d = 1.89$.

Hence,

$$W = C_d \, a \, \frac{P_u}{\sqrt{T_u}} \sqrt{\frac{2\gamma}{R(\gamma - 1)}} \sqrt{\left(\frac{P_d}{P_u}\right)^{2/\gamma} - \left(\frac{P_d}{P_u}\right)^{\frac{\gamma + 1}{\gamma}}} \tag{5.34}$$

$$= C_d \, C_m \, a \, \frac{P_u}{\sqrt{T_u}}$$

for comparison purposes, the equivalent relationship for oil is,

$$Q = C_d \, a \sqrt{\frac{2}{\rho}} \sqrt{P_u - P_d}$$

If equation (5.34) is differentiated to find the maximum, then for air,

$$\left(\frac{P_d}{P_u}\right) = \left(\frac{2}{\gamma + 1}\right)^{\frac{\gamma}{\gamma - 1}} = 0.528$$

representing the condition for choked flow and,

$$C_m = \sqrt{\frac{2\gamma}{R(\gamma-1)}} \sqrt{\left(\frac{P_d}{P_u}\right)^{\frac{2}{\gamma}} - \left(\frac{P_d}{P_u}\right)^{\frac{\gamma+1}{\gamma}}}$$

On the other hand when,

$$\frac{P_d}{P_u} \leq \left(\frac{2}{\gamma+1}\right)^{\frac{\gamma}{\gamma-1}}$$

then,

$$C_m = \sqrt{\frac{2\gamma}{R(\gamma+1)}} \left(\frac{2}{\gamma+1}\right)^{\frac{1}{\gamma-1}} = 0.04$$

Hence,

$$W = C_d \, C_m \, a \, \frac{P_u}{\sqrt{T_u}} \tag{5.35}$$

The characteristics of C_m are shown in Figure 5.25 and can be used for design calculations.

EXERCISES

5.1. Determine the displacement of a spool 6 mm in diameter, when the open annular regions produce a flow of 1.1 l/s at a pressure difference of 0.5 MPa, across the valve.

5.2. A simple hydraulic actuator consists of a four-way valve and a ram. Each of the valve's two control ports has an area gain of 1.27 mm² for each mm travel of the spool. The oil density is 692 kg/m³, and the oil supply pressure is 6.89 MPa. The effective diameter of the ram piston is 76.2 mm. Determine:

   (a) The pressure drop per control port to ensure maximum power transmission to the ram.

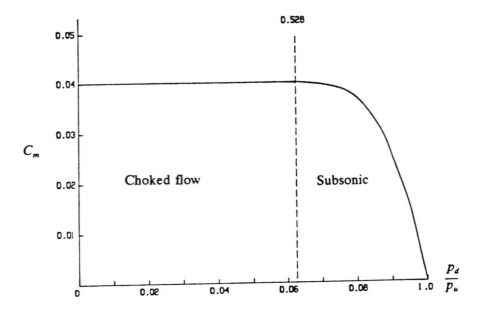

Figure 5.25 Air Flow Coefficient

(b) The oil flow under these conditions, if the spool displacement is 2.54 mm.

(c) The piston speed and output force under these conditions.

5.3. For the circuit shown in Figure 5.26,

Piston diameter	57.2 mm
Rod diameter	34.9 mm
Orifice A diameter	2.5 mm
Orifice B diameter	1.9 mm

Determine:

1. The pressure drop across each orifice, when under load conditions.

2. The speed of the piston, if an external load of 22 kN is being pulled along.

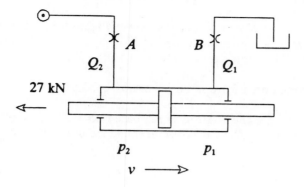

Figure 5.26 Figure for Exercise 5.3

5.4. The steady flow characteristics of a 4/2 directional control valve can be approximated to $Q^2 = K\Delta p$, across each side of the valve. The double-acting, double-ended ram attached to the valve is used to move a mass of 2500 kg on a horizontal slide. The effective piston area is 3×10^3 mm². Also opposing the motion is a constant force of 500 N and a viscous resistance of 3.0 N/(m/s). A flow test carried out on the valve shows that for a flow of 500 ml/s, the pressure drop is 2.5 MPa. If the supply pressure is 10 MPa, determine the velocity and acceleration of the load at maximum power output from the ram.

5.5. A single-ended ram is controlled by a solenoid actuated valve. The ram has to move a mass of 800 kg on a horizontal plane. There is a pipe 6 m long with an internal diameter of 20 mm, connecting the valve to the outlet of the pump. If all the other pipes are short, determine:

(a) The pressure necessary to impart an acceleration of 30 m/s², on the load. The effective piston diameter is 40 mm. Ignore all other losses.

(b) With an operating pressure of 8 MPa, what is the flow conductance value for the solenoid operated valve that will maintain a steady speed of 2 m/s at the load?

(c) If the voltage to the solenoid valve is shut off, when the flow is 3000 cm³/s, what is the magnitude of the shock pressure in the pipe, and what is the propagation time of the pressure pulse in the pipe?

Assume the flow through the valve is approximated to orifice flow.

5.6. A hydraulic ram is controlled by a four-way valve (Figure 5.18). It is required to make the system work into a constant load of 3558 N in either direction, with a velocity of 0.32 m/s. The supply pressure is 10.3 MPa. Determine:

(a) The required piston area for optimum working conditions.

(b) The size of orifices for the control ports, based on a 30% uncovered area requirement. What will the valve displacement be under this opening?

CHAPTER 6

Hydraulic pumps and motors

6.1 Introduction

The hydraulic pump and motor are some of the main elements of hydraulic drives, and are used to convert mechanical power (torque x angular velocity) into fluid power (pressure x flow) in the case of the pump, and vice versa for the motor.
In order to provide efficient handling of fluid, these components are designed for positive displacement operation. This means that the suction and delivery are separated by distinct pumping chambers, so that discrete blocks of fluid are forced to circulate in the system [15]. The other way of moving fluid is to use impeller-type units, as are commonly used in air conditioning and heating equipment. These non-positive displacement or hydrodynamic designs are not capable of handling high pressure, and are normally limited to around 200 kPa.

The simplest type of positive displacement or hydrostatic pump is the single-acting manually operated hand pump shown in Figure 6.1.

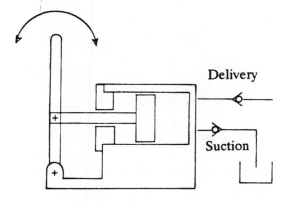

Figure. 6.1 Manual Hand Pump

The important feature of any pump is the valving; one non-return valve on the suction side and the other on the delivery side. Like all fluid systems, it is necessary to prime the pump, that is, the removal of air, before any useful operation can be achieved.

The other types of pumps are externally driven, usually by fixed-speed electric motors, although the power source can be an internal combustion engine, in which case the speed may vary. Normally if variable flow is required, it is better to provide this feature within the pump, than use a variable speed drive motor.

There are a wide variety of designs of hydraulic pumps and motors, and some of these are summarized in Table 6.1. Most pumps and motors are essentially the same type of design, and can therefore be used in reverse roll for emergencies. The main difference is in the bearing design. The exception is the vane pump which cannot be used as a vane motor.

Some examples of pump arrangements are shown in Figures 6.2, 6.3 and 6.4. Note also that rams can be thought of as linear motors.

The gear pump or motor (Figure 6.2), operates by filling the space between two consecutive teeth and the outer casing with liquid.

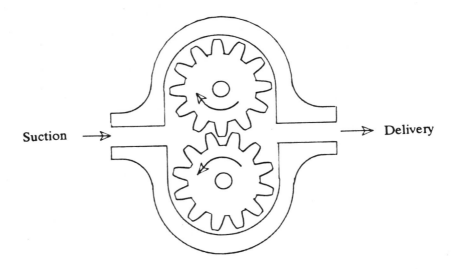

Figure 6.2 External Gear Pump

This is then carried around the casing to the outlet side where the oil is pressurized as two teeth engage. If the pump speed is too high, then it is possible for cavitation to occur, since the exit velocity of the oil jet can result in a very low local pressure (Bernoulli's Law).   This will cause a great deal of noise and eventually damage the teeth.

Table 6.1

	Fixed		Variable	
Gear	Piston	Vane	Vane	Piston
External	Radial		Direct	Radial
Internal Crescent Gerotor	Axial		Pilot control Axial Swash plate	
	Bent axis		Bent axis	

Gear pumps and motors are normally limited to below 14 MPa operating pressure and speeds of 2400 rpm. Maximum flow capacity would be 0.5 m³/min. The main advantages are the simple trouble-free design and low cost.

The vane pump or motor develops pressure or torque by hydraulic pressure acting on the exposed surfaces of the vanes (Figure 6.3).   As the shaft turns, the vanes follow the contours of the casing. Initially, springs provide the only force to hold the vanes against the casing, but as the speed increases, the vanes are forced radially outwards under the influence of centrifugal force. The sliding action of the vanes in their respective grooves forms variable volume chambers to carry the fluid from the inlet to the delivery side. Typical operating oil pressures are up to 17 MPa with speeds up to 4000 rpm. Maximum flow delivery can be up to 0.8 m³/min.

Piston pumps or motors are commonly used in both fixed and variable flow configurations. The performance is much higher than either of the other two designs, and so is the cost. In the configuration shown in Figure 6.4, flow is controlled by the angle of the swash plate.

In variable flow pumps, this plate can be shifted manually with an external lever or can be under the control of a sophisticated servo control system. The maximum swash plate angle normally does not exceed 30°. Operating pressures of 70 MPa and higher are available, with flows up to 1.5 m³/min. Piston motors can be operated at speeds up to 12 000 rpm.

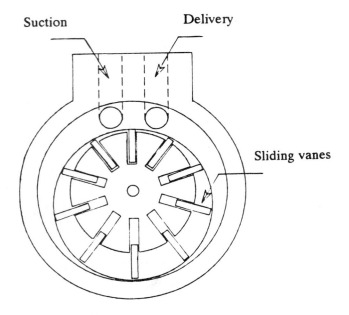

Figure 6.3 Vane Pump

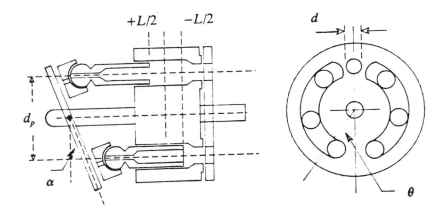

Figure 6.4a Piston Pump

6.2 Theory

6.2.1 Displacement

A convenient way to characterize positive displacement pumps or motors is in terms of displacement. The ideal positive displacement machine displaces a particular volume of fluid for every revolution of the shaft. The ideal flow, without any losses, will be,

$$Q_i = D_p N = D_m N \tag{6.1}$$

The subscripts p and m indicate pump and motor, respectively. Hence, if V is the swept volume of the pump or motor per radian of the shaft rotation, an alternative way to express displacement is,

$$D_p = D_m = 2\pi V \text{ m}^3/\text{rev} \tag{6.2}$$

The ideal swept volume can then be calculated from the geometry of the pump or motor, and in this case has units of m³/rad.

6.2.2 Gear configuration

Referring to Figure 6.2, the following geometric definitions apply to spur gear arrangements:

d_a diameter of addendum circle
d_d diameter of dedendum circle
w width of a gear tooth

If the two gears were to mesh perfectly, then the quantity of fluid that would be carried by the two gears in one revolution of the shaft would be the displacement,

$$D_p = \frac{w\pi}{4}(d_a^2 - d_d^2) \tag{6.3}$$

and therefore the ideal flow is,

$$Q_i = \frac{w\pi}{4}(d_a^2 - d_d^2)N$$

This assumes that half the area between the two circles for each gear is taken up by metal.

6.2.3 Vane configuration

Referring to Figure 6.3, the following geometric definitions are used;

a	vane plate thickness
w	width of vane plate
d_c	internal diameter of the casing
d_r	diameter of the drive shaft
e	eccentricity between centre line of the casing and the drive shaft
n	number of vanes

The maximum volume between the rotor holding the vanes and the casing must be,

$$D_p = \left(\frac{\pi d_c^2}{4} - \frac{\pi d_r^2}{4}\right)w$$

$$= \frac{\pi w}{4}(d_c - d_r)(d_c + d_r)$$

The eccentricity is,

$$e = \frac{d_c - d_r}{2}$$

Hence,

$$D_p = \frac{\pi w}{2}(d_c + d_r)e \tag{6.4}$$

There should be a correction for the amount of volume taken up by the metal in the vanes.

6.2.4 Axial piston configuration

Referring to Figure 6.4a, the following geometric definitions apply:

l piston stroke
d_p piston pitch circle diameter
d piston diameter
α swash plate angle
θ shaft rotation

For each piston in its cylinder,

$$l = 2 \times \frac{d_p}{2} \tan \alpha \tag{6.5}$$

The angle θ determines the angular displacement of the drive shaft, while the swash plate angle α determines the amplitude of the piston stroke.

The volume displaced by one piston is,

$$\text{Volume} = \left(\frac{\pi d^2}{4}\right) d_p \tan \alpha \cos \theta \tag{6.6}$$

The total displacement will be equation (6.5) multiplied by the number of pistons n in the pump or motor.

In Figure 6.4b, it is assumed that one piston is fully filled with oil and is about to discharge through the valve plate to the delivery line. The valving is timed, so that for a short time the oil is trapped in the cylinder as the piston is about to start its down stroke. All the other pistons are in various degrees of filling or emptying. Most pumps and motors of this type are designed such that the body of the unit is rotated, dragging the pistons around the inclined plane of the swash plate. The valve plate is fixed.

EXAMPLE 6.1

Find the swash plate angle of an axial piston pump which delivers 0.06 m³/min of oil when the input shaft angular velocity is 1740 rpm. The pump has seven, 12 mm diameter pistons arranged around a 10 cm pitch circle. Assume that the pump has no losses.

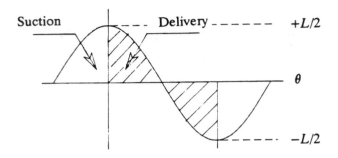

Figure 6.4b Pumping Cycle for One Piston

From equations (6.5) and (6.6),

$$Q_i = D_p = Nn \frac{\pi d^2}{4} d_p \tan \alpha$$

$$0.06 = 1740 \times 7 \times 3.14 \times \frac{(12 \times 10^{-3})^2}{4} \times 0.1 \times \tan \alpha$$

$$\tan \alpha = \frac{0.06}{0.1377} = 0.435\,73$$

$$\alpha = 23.54°$$

6.2.5 Flow relationships

The ideal flow, Q_i, derived in equation (6.7), is not the same as the actual flow Q_a, because of leakage; therefore for a pump,

$$Q_a = Q_i - Q_l = D_p N - Q_l$$

In the case of a hydraulic motor, enough fluid must be put into the unit to provide the shaft speed and make up the leakage,

$$Q_m = D_m N + Q_l$$

Leakage flow is very difficult to calculate and is usually determined by experimental testing of each pump or motor design. It is a function of mean clearance, h, fluid viscosity and pressure,

$$Q_a = D_p N - f\left(\frac{h^3}{\mu}\right) p_p \tag{6.7}$$

The leakage is referred to as slip flow, and is defined in terms of a slip flow coefficient,

$$C_l^p = f\left(\frac{h^3}{\mu}\right)$$

so that

$$Q_a = D_p N - C_l^p p_p \tag{6.8}$$

Figure 6.5 shows an experimental plot of pump delivery against speed for different pressures, based on equation (6.8). When the speed is zero, $N = 0$,

$$Q_a = Q_i = -C_l^p$$

indicating an experimental method of determining the leakage as a function of pressure. Equation (6.8) represents a straight line, the general form of which is $y = mx + c$, for each value of p_p, and therefore the slope must be the D_p value for the pump. Similar information can be determined for a motor, where the sign of the leakage coefficient in equation (6.8) becomes positive.

6.2.6 Torque relationships

The inputs to a pump are torque T_a and angular velocity ω, of the shaft. This

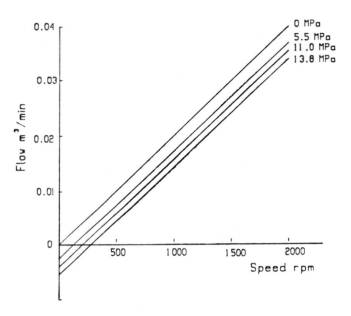

Figure 6.5 Pump Flow Characteristics

mechanical power is converted into flow out of the pump and a delivery pressure p_p. Hence under ideal conditions, all the input mechanical power is converted into output fluid power. The input work done is the torque T_i turning the shaft by a small angle $d\theta$. This results in a volume of fluid, $D_p/2\pi.d\theta$. Power is the rate of doing work, hence,

$$\frac{d}{dt}(T_i d\theta) = \frac{d}{dt}\left(\frac{D_p}{2\pi} d\theta\, p_p\right)$$

or ideally,

$$T_i = \frac{D_p}{2\pi} P_p$$

However, some of this torque will have to be used to overcome friction. This is measured by the drag coefficient, C_d, which is dependent on both viscous and coulomb friction, and is therefore better determined experimentally. The actual torque is given by,

$$T_a = T_i + C_d^p N$$

$$= \frac{D_p}{2\pi} P_p + C_d^p N \qquad (6.9)$$

Figure 6.6 shows a plot of input torque to a pump against shaft speed for different pressures, based on equation (6.9). When the speed is zero, the intersect with the y axis is,

$$T_a = \frac{D_p}{2\pi} P_p$$

This represents the breakaway torque required to start the pump shaft rotating, and the slope is the drag coefficient C_d. Similar information can be obtained for a motor by changing the sign of the drag coefficient in equation (6.9) to negative.

6.3 Pump and motor efficiencies

While the volume that can theoretically be pumped per revolution can be calculated from the pump geometry, the pump never quite delivers that amount of fluid in practice, due to leakage. This can be defined in terms of volumetric efficiency,

$$\eta_p^v = \frac{Q_a}{Q_i} = \frac{D_p - C_l^p P_p}{D_p N}$$

giving,

$$\eta_p^v = 1 - \frac{C_i^p \, P_p}{D_p \, N} \tag{6.10}$$

It can be seen from equation (6.10) that, at constant speed, the volumetric efficiency decreases with increasing pressure; while at constant pressure, the volumetric efficiency increases with increasing speed.

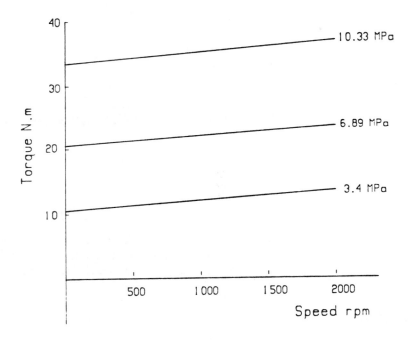

Figure 6.6 Pump Torque Characteristics

The mechanical efficiency, on the other hand, is controlled by the friction between the moving parts of the pump,

$$\eta_p^m = \frac{D_p P_p}{2\pi T_p}$$

giving,

$$\eta_p^m = \cfrac{1}{1 + \cfrac{2\pi\,C_d^p\,N}{D_p P_p}} \qquad\qquad (6.11)$$

From this relationship, it can be seen that at constant speed, the mechanical efficiency improves as the pressure is increased. The overall efficiency of a pump or motor is simply the product of the volumetric and mechanical efficiencies. Table 6.2 shows a summary of typical values for different pump designs. The values are similar for motors.

Table 6.2

Type	Working Pressure (MPa)	Shaft Speed (rpm)	Overall Efficiency (%)
Gear	4–10	500–3000	60–80
Vane	5–10	500–3000	65–80
Piston(axial)	20–2	200–2000	85–98
Piston(radial)	35–65	200–2000	85–95

EXAMPLE 6.2

A gear pump has the following dimensions:

> Addendum diameter d_a = 120 mm
> Dedendum diameter d_d = 080 mm
> Width of tooth $\quad w$ = 025 mm

Tests show that the volumetric and mechanical efficiencies of the pump are, respectively, 0.8 and 0.9 when the shaft speed is 1000 rpm and the delivery pressure is 10 MPa. Determine the delivery flow rate and the leakage flow under these conditions.

Since it can be assumed that leakage is proportional to pressure and that mechanical losses are proportional to the angular velocity of the pump shaft determine the volumetric, mechanical efficiencies and the input power required to drive the pump at 1500 rpm, while developing 14 MPa. At 1000 rpm,

$$D_p = \frac{\pi}{4} w (d_a^2 - d_d^2)$$

$$= \frac{3.14}{4} \times 0.025 (0.120^2 - 0.08^2)$$

$$= 1.57 \times 10^{-4} \text{ m}^3/\text{rev}$$

$$Q_i = D_p N = 1.57 \times 10^{-4} \times 10^3 = 0.157 \text{ m}^3/\text{min}$$

Now,

$$\eta = 0.8$$

$$Q_a = 0.157 \times 0.8 = 0.1256 \text{ m}^3/\text{min}$$

$$Q_l = Q_i - Q_a = 0.1570 - 0.1256 = 0.0314 \text{ m}^3/\text{min}$$

Since $Q_l \propto p$, then,

$$\frac{0.0314}{Q_l} = \frac{10}{14}$$

$$Q_l = 0.043\,96 \text{ m}^3/\text{min} \qquad \text{at} \qquad 14 \text{ MPa}$$

at 1500 rpm,

$$\eta_v^p = 1 - \frac{Q_l}{D_p} N$$

$$= 1 - \frac{0.043\,96}{1500 \times 1.57 \times 10^{-4}} = 0.81$$

Now,

$$\eta_m^p = 0.9 \text{ at } 1000 \text{ rpm}$$

$$T_i = \frac{D_p p_p}{2\pi} = \frac{1.57 \times 10^{-4} \times 10 \times 10^6}{2 \times 3.14} = 250 \text{ N.m}$$

$$T_a = \frac{250}{0.9} = 278 \text{ N.m}$$

The torque due to mechanical losses will be,

$$T_d = T_a - T_i = 28 \text{ N.m}$$

and since $T_d \, \alpha \, \omega$,

$$\frac{28}{T_d} = \frac{1000}{1500}$$

$$T_d = 42 \text{ N.m at } 1500 \text{ rpm}$$

Now at 14 MPa,

$$T_i = \frac{D_p p_p}{2\pi} = \frac{1.57 \times 10^{-4} \times 14 \times 10^6}{2 \times 3.14}$$

$$= 350 \text{ N.m}$$

and,

$$\eta_m^p = \frac{350}{(350 + 42)} = 0.89$$

The input power is,

$$T_a N = \frac{(350 + 42) \times 1500 \times 2 \times 3.14}{60} = 61.5 \text{ kW}$$

6.4 Pump set design

The energy source for any fluid power system must originate from a pump set. Hence this is an important component of the system, which needs to provide clean, cool, oil at the specified pressure and flow requirements. A typical design is hown in Figure 6.7. The motor driving the pump is usually electric running at 1740 rpm, for industrial applications, but could also be an IC or diesel engine. The outlet from the fixed displacement pump is piped to a relief valve, allowing the working pressure to be selected. The non-return valve N prevents flow being forced back into the pump, as a result of pressure pulses. This is especially important for vane pumps, since they cannot be driven in reverse as motors.

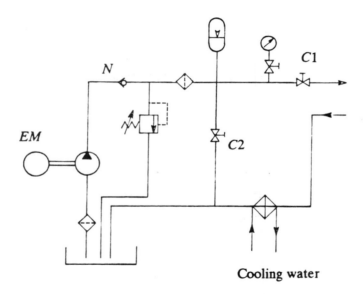

Figure 6.7 Basic Pump Set Circuit

It also helps to stiffen the circuit. An accumulator (see Chapter 7) is included to smooth the pressure pulses developed in the pump, but will also provide additional flow for short periods, as a result of high transient flow demands. It is wise to include a shut-off valve, *C1*, to prevent oil spillage if the delivery line has to be disconnected from the main circuit. Shut-off valve *C2* allows the accumulator to be discharged safely. The filter can be placed in several positions around the circuit, as discussed in Chapter 4, but in this case, it has been placed in the delivery line. The suction line has a strainer to remove any large debris, but care must be taken to ensure that neither it nor any other component in this line creates significant pressure loss.

The pressure gauge should be placed near the end of the line to show the true pressure entering the circuit. It also should have a shut-off valve to avoid damage, and should only be open when a measurement is required.

A typical tank design is shown in Figure 6.8. It is not just a container for the oil, but serves an important function in the preventive maintenance of the system. It must hold enough oil to meet the circuit demand when all the rams are extended and motors are running at full speed, and still leave plenty in the tank. It must act as a heat exchanger to cool the oil and also to allow time for contaminants such as foam and dirt to settle out.

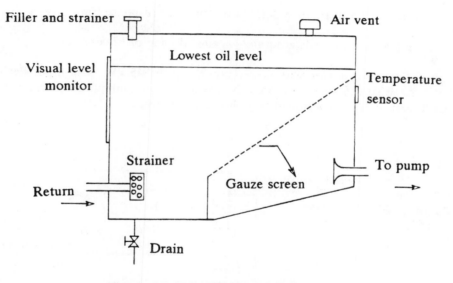

Figure 6.8 Tank Design Features

The size of the tank should be at least three times the volume delivered by the pump in 1 min, and may be as large as six times if there are a number of valves in the circuit to generate heat. The estimated control of heat in hydraulic circuits is discussed in more detail in Chapter 8.

6.5 The hydrostatic transmission

The hydrostatic transmission is a hydraulic system consisting of a positive displacement pump and one or more motors. It is widely used by industry and is available in many different configurations. The principle of operation is quite different than that used in hydrodynamic drives. In this case, non-positive displacement devices are used and dynamic conversion of fluid kinetic energy is used rather than hydrostatic pressure. This type of coupling is commonly used in vehicle transmissions.

The main advantages of the hydrostatic transmission are:

1. High power output to unit weight ratio.

2. Can be stalled without damage.

3. Infinitely variable speed and torque in the forward and reverse directions over the full power range.

4. Low inertia of rotating parts permitting fast response times.

5. Holds preset speeds accurately against driving or braking loads.

These drives are available with power ratings up to 745 kW, with many design variations. Figure 6.9 shows a basic hydrostatic drive configuration, where the bidirectional motor is controlled by a directional valve.

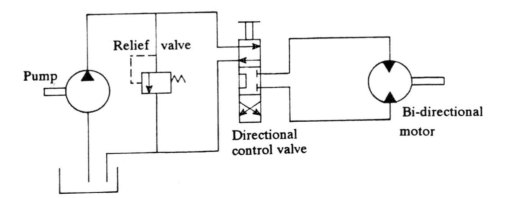

Figure 6.9 Basic Hydrostatic Transmission

This particular arrangement is referred to as open circuit and fixed speed. In the open circuit design, the exhausting fluid from the motor is discharged directly into the tank. This means that the low-pressure side of the circuit is always open to atmospheric pressure. In the closed circuit design, the discharge from the motor is piped directly back to the inlet side of the pump, and no tank is needed in the primary circuit. Figure 6.10 shows a typical arrangement where the low-pressure side is controlled through a small charging pump, which also provides make up for leakage. In the closed circuit drive, the motor direction can be controlled several ways, for example by using a reversible pump. In the open circuit design, directional control is confined to the directional valve.

When using variable displacement pumps and motors, servo control loops can be incorporated for precision control.

Referring to Figure 6.10, the output flow from the pump is,

$$Q_p = D_p N_p - C_l^p p_p \qquad (6.12)$$

For the hydraulic motor, the output speed is given by,

$$N_m = \frac{1}{D_m}(Q_m - C_l^m p_m) \qquad (6.13)$$

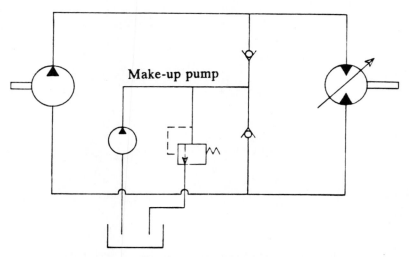

Figure 6.10 Closed Circuit Hydrostatic Transmission

and the motor also provides torque, given by,

$$T_m = \frac{D_m}{2\pi} P_m - C_d^m N_m \tag{6.14}$$

Normally, the pump shaft speed is fixed by the electric drive motor; the performance of the output torque T_m and speed, N, are of most interest.
From equation (6.13),

$$P_m = \frac{Q_m - D_m N_m}{C_l^m} \tag{6.15}$$

If it is assumed that there are no pressure losses through the pipe work and directional control valve, then $p_p = p_m$, and equation (6.12) can be rewritten as,

$$Q_P = D_p N_p - C_l^p \left(\frac{Q_m - D_m N_m}{C_l^m} \right)$$

$$= D_p N_p - \frac{C_l^p}{C_l^m} Q_m + \frac{C_l^p}{C_l^m} D_m N_m$$

and since $Q_p = Q_m$,

$$Q_P = \frac{D_p N_p + \dfrac{C_l^p}{C_l^m} D_m N_m}{\left(1 + \dfrac{C_l^p}{C_l^m} \right)} \tag{6.16}$$

from equation (6.15),

$$P_m = P_p = \frac{Q_p}{C_l^m} - \frac{D_m}{C_l^m} N_m$$

and substituting from equation (6.16),

$$P_m = \frac{D_p N_p + \dfrac{C_l^p}{C_l^m} D_m N_m}{C_l^m \left(1 + \dfrac{C_l^p}{C_l^m}\right)} - \frac{D_m}{C_l^m} N_m$$

The torque relationship is then obtained from equation (6.14), and the terms associated with the pump speed and the motor speed are separated out,

$$T_m = \frac{D_m D_p}{2\pi (C_l^m + C_l^p)} N_p$$

$$- \left[\frac{D_m^2}{2\pi C_l^m} - \frac{D_m}{2\pi} \left(\frac{\dfrac{C_l^p}{C_l^m} D_m}{C_l^m + C_l^p} \right) + C_d^m \right] N_m \tag{6.17}$$

It can be seen from equation (6.17), that for a fixed pump speed N_p, the motor speed can be controlled by varying the leakage C_l^p and/or C_l^m artificially using a bleed, or by varying D_p and/or D_m using variable displacement pumps and/or motors.

The bleed approach for speed control is limited to about 40 kW of power demand, due to energy wastage and oil heating.

6.5.1 Effects of compressibility and load

The torque output from the motor T_m can be subjected to a range of different types of loading, for example:

(a) Constant Torque

(b) Pure Inertia

(c) Pure Inertia and Friction

The worst design case is usually (b), since it involves rapid acceleration and deceleration. When a closed loop control system is involved in the design, then this case can lead to stability problems. Inertia loading also results in oil compressibility, due to rapid rates of change of pressure, hence equation (6.12) has an additional term,

$$Q_a = D_p N_p - C_i^p P_p - \frac{V}{N} \frac{dp_p}{dt}$$

$$= D_p N_p - \left(C_i^p + \frac{V}{N} s \right) P_p$$

(6.18)

where V is the total volume on the high-pressure side of the circuit, N is the bulk modulus of the oil, not to be confused with shaft speed, and $s \equiv d/dt$ is the Laplace variable. For the circuit shown in Figure 6.7, and since $Q_p = Q_m$,

$$D_p N_p - \left(C_i^p - \frac{V}{N} s \right) P_p = D_m N_m + C_i^m P_m$$

and since $p_p = p_m$, the motor speed is,

$$N_m = \frac{1}{D_m} \left[D_p N_p - \left((C_i^p + C_i^m) - \frac{V}{N} s \right) P_p \right]$$

(6.19)

For loading as defined by case (c),

$$T_m = (Is + b) N_m$$

(6.20)

using equation (6.11) as a guide, the mechanical efficiency for a motor will be the reciprocal of this relationship,

$$\eta_m^m = \frac{2\pi\, T_m}{D_m P_m}$$

therefore the pressure at the motor is given by,

$$P_m = \frac{2\pi}{D_m\, \eta_m^m}\, [Is + b]\, N_m \tag{6.21}$$

using equations (6.18) and (6.21); and the fact that the motor compressibility is included in equation (6.18), so that,

$$P_m = \frac{Q_a}{C_l^m} - \frac{D_m N_m}{C_l^m}$$

This allows a block diagram to be drawn as shown in Figure 6.9.

If equation (6.21) is now substituted into equation (6.19), and remembering that for this particular circuit $p_p = p_m$,

$$N_m = \frac{1}{D_m}\left[D_p N_p - \left(\frac{2\pi\left(C_l^p + C_l^m\right) I}{D_m\, \eta_m^m}s \right.\right.$$

$$\left.\left. - \frac{2\pi\left(C_l^p + C_l^m\right) b}{D_m\, \eta_m^m} - \frac{2\pi\, VI}{ND_m\, \eta_m^m}s^2 - \frac{2\pi\, Vb}{ND_m\, \eta_m^m}s \right) N_m \right]$$

rearranging,

$$\left(\frac{\eta_m^m ND_m D_p}{2\pi IV}\right) N_p = \left[s^2 + \left(\frac{N}{V}\left(C_l^p + C_l^m\right) + \frac{b}{I}\right)s\right.$$

$$\left. + \left(\frac{bN}{IV}\left(C_l^p + C_l^m\right) + \frac{\eta_m^m ND_m^2}{2\pi IV}\right)\right] N_m$$

which can also be expressed in more general form as,

$$KN_p = \left[s^2 + 2\zeta\omega_n s + \omega_n^2\right] N_m \tag{6.22}$$

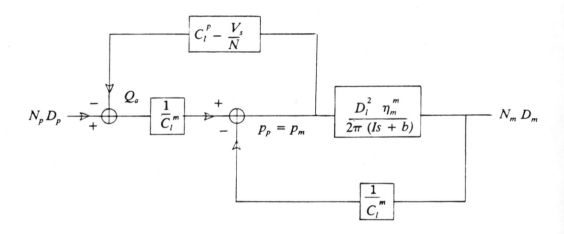

Figure 6.11 Block Diagram for a Hydrostatic Transmission

The natural frequency of this transmission is given by,

$$f_n = D_m \sqrt{\frac{N\eta_m^m}{8\pi^3 IV}\left[\frac{2\pi b\left(C_l^p + C_l^m\right)}{\eta_m^m D_m^2} + 1\right]} \tag{6.23}$$

and the damping ratio is given by,

$$\zeta = \frac{1}{4\pi f_n}\left[\frac{N}{V}\left(C_l^p + C_l^m\right) + \frac{b}{I}\right] \tag{6.24}$$

in which it is seen that part of the damping is a result of leakage and the rest is due to friction between moving parts of the pump and motor.

EXAMPLE 6.3

A variable capacity hydraulic pump is used to power a fixed capacity motor. The specifications for these units are as follows:

Pump
Maximum displacement	$= 1.64 \times 10^{-4}$ m^3/rev
Drive shaft speed	$= 25$ rev/s
Leakage coefficient	$= 1.8 \times 10^{-5}$ m^3/MPa.s
Mechanical efficiency	$= 85\%$

Motor
Displacement	$= 6.5 \times 10^{-5}$ m^3/rev
Leakage coefficient	$= 9 \times 10^{-6}$ m^3/MPa.s
Mechanical efficiency	$= 88\%$
Inertia load	$= 1.5$ kg.m^2

Losses in the piping and compressibility effects can be ignored. Determine:

1. The acceleration of the hydraulic motor, to increase the motors speed from rest to 33 rev/s when the pump is operating at 60% of maximum displacement

2. The power output drawn from the electric motor driving the pump under the above conditions.

3. How long will it take the motor to reach its steady state speed, if the pump displacement is given a step change from 0 to 50% of its maximum value.

1. Since there is no bleed flow,

$$Q_{p,m} = D_p N_p - C'_p P_p = D_m N_m + C'_m P_m$$

$$P_p = \frac{D_p N_p - D_m N_m}{\left(C'_p + C'_m\right)} = P_m$$

$$P_p = \frac{0.6 \times 1.64 \times 10^{-4} \times \dfrac{1740}{60} - 6.5 \times 10^{-5} \times 33}{(1.8 \times 10^{-5} + 9.0 \times 10^{-6})} = 26.24 \text{ MPa}$$

Now,

$$T_m = I \frac{d\omega_m}{dt}$$

$$\eta^m_m = \frac{2\pi T_m}{p D_m}$$

So that,

$$\frac{d\omega_m}{dt} = \frac{\eta^m_m \times p \times D_m}{2\pi \times I}$$

$$= \frac{0.88 \times 26.24 \times 10^6 \times 6.5 \times 10^{-5}}{2 \times 3.14 \times 1.5} = 159.3 \text{ rev/s}^2$$

2. The power W is given by,

$$W = \frac{p \times Q}{\eta^0_p} = \frac{p \times N_p \times D_p}{\eta^m_p}$$

$$W = \cfrac{26.24 \times 10^6 \times \cfrac{1740}{60} \times 1.64 \times 10^{-4} \times 0.6}{0.85}$$

$$= 88.09 \ \text{kW}$$

3. Referring to equation (6.22) and since we are dealing with steady-state speed, the s^2 term vanishes,

$$\left(\frac{\eta_m^m N D_m D_p}{2\pi I V}\right) N_p = (2\zeta \omega_n s + \omega_n^2) \ N_m$$

Now,

$$\omega_n^2 = \frac{\eta_m^m N D_m^2}{2\pi I V}$$

Therefore,

$$\left(\frac{D_p}{D_m}\right) N_p = \left(\frac{2\zeta}{\omega_n} s + 1\right) N_m$$

This is a first-order equation, therefore the time constant will be $2\zeta/\omega_n$. Using equation (6.24), and noting that $b = 0$,

$$\zeta = \frac{1}{2\omega_n}\left[\frac{N}{V}\left(C_l^p + C_l^m\right)\right]$$

Then,

$$\frac{2\zeta}{\omega_n} = \frac{2}{2\omega_n^2}\left[\frac{N}{V}\left(C_l^p + C_l^m\right)\right]$$

and,

$$\frac{2\zeta}{\omega_n} = \frac{2\pi I}{\zeta_m^m D_m^2}\left(C_l^p + C_l^m\right)$$

$$= \frac{2 \times 3.14 \times 1.5 \times (1.8 \times 10^{-5} + 9 \times 10^{-6}) \times 10^{-6}}{0.88 \times (6.5 \times 10^{-5})^2}$$

$$= 0.068 \text{ s}$$

The time taken to reach steady-state speed is four times the time constant, 4 x 0.068 = 0.272 s.

EXERCISES

6.1. The maximum circuit pressure for a hydrostatic transmission is 8.26 MPa. The maximum displacement of the variable capacity pump is 1.148×10^{-4} m^3/rev, and for the fixed capacity motor is 1.476×10^{-4} m^3/rev. The pump is directly coupled to an electric motor and operates at a constant speed of 1000 rpm. If the overall efficiency of the pump and motor is 84%, and the torque efficiency of each is 90%, determine:

(a) The maximum motor speed and the power developed, when the electric motor runs at 1000 rpm.
(b) The torque supplied to the pump from the electric motor.
(c) The slip flow coefficient for the pump and motor.
(d) The percentage power loss for the system.

6.2. A hydraulic transmission operates on 7 MPa system pressure, and has the following performance characteristics;

Parameter	Pump	Motor
D_p m^3/rev	0.82×10^{-3}	?
η_v %	82	92
η_m %	88	90
N rpm	500	400

Find: (a) The displacement of the motor.
       (b) The motor torque output.

6.3. A hydraulic transmission consists of a variable displacement pump and a fixed displacement motor, having a combined leakage of 10^{-2} l/min/bar. The total load at the motor shaft is 300 N.M.s^2 and the motor displacement is 25 ml/rad. The maximum motor speed is 200 rpm, and the motor is to be capable of accelerating from rest to this maximum speed in 20 s.

(a) Find the system pressure, neglecting losses in the pipework.
(b) Calculate the pump delivery.
(c) If the overall pump efficiency is 85%, what electric motor power is required to drive the pump?

6.4. Draw a circuit for a direct acting hydraulic press, comprising a ram, a constant speed high-pressure pump and a control valve. Include any safety devices. It is found that the ram piston diameter is 203.3 mm on the full area side. The hydraulic ram is required to exert a thrust of 1.295 MN. The pump has a capacity of 1.6 x 10^{-5} m^3/rev and runs at 1470 rpm. If the volumetric efficiency of the pump is 96%, estimate the speed at which the press operates. When the press is exerting its maximum thrust of 1.295 MN, what would be the system pressure, and the power output from the pump? Determine the overall efficiency.

6.5. A hydraulic pump drives a hydraulic motor supplying 3.7 kW of power to a machine, when the shaft speed is 500 rpm. The pump delivery pressure is 5.2 MPa and there is a pressure drop of 0.04 MPa in the pipes joining the pump to the motor. Assuming volumetric and mechanical efficiencies of 90% for both units, determine:

(a) The displacement of the motor.
(b) The delivery rate of the pump.
(c) The power required to drive the pump.

6.6. A hydraulic pump has the following operating characteristics;

Supply pressure	20 MPa
Output flow	0.5 x 10^{-3} m^3/s
Shaft speed	1440 rpm
Volumetric efficiency	95%
Mechanical efficiency	85%

A similar motor fails in a piece of production machinery, so it is decided to use this pump to replace the motor, until the new one arrives. Calculate:

(a) The ideal and actual torque output of the pump used as a motor.
(b) The ideal and actual power output.

CHAPTER 7

Accumulators and their application

7.1 Fundamentals

The accumulator has a number of important uses, for example:

1. To provide standby power, to reduce pump size requirements and hence save energy.

2. To provide standby power for emergency situations, such as a pump failure, thus making enough power available to allow the equipment to return to a safe condition.

3. To control shock pressure loading in hydraulic lines, due, for example, to the rapid closing of valves.

4. To provide a filter to reduce ripple flow from a pump.

5. To provide make-up volume during thermal expansion.

In Figure 7.1, it can be seen that this component has gas on one side of a flexible barrier and oil on the other. Energy is stored by compressing the gas, as a consequence of pumping oil into the lower chamber.

Accumulator size estimates under isothermal conditions are based on Boyle's Law. The three most important conditions for accumulator operation are shown in Figure 7.2.

The gas precharge pressure is normally selected at $1/n$th of the final maximum pressure, where n depends on the application. Some guidelines are summarized in Table 6.1. It is always advisable to use nitrogen as the charge gas, to ensure safe operation.

The stages in the operation of an accumulator are defined by:

p_1V_1 Gas precharge pressure and volume, where V_1 is the size of the accumulator.

p_2V_2 Gas charge pressure and volume, after the hydraulic pump has been turned on.

p_3V_3 Minimum pressure required by the circuit. The gas volume will be greater than the oil volume at this stage.

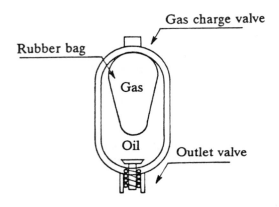

Figure 7.1 Bag Type Accumulator

For an isothermal process,

$$\frac{p_1V_1}{T_1} = \frac{p_2V_2}{T_2} = \frac{p_3V_3}{T_3}$$

and if the expansion or compression of the gas in the accumulator takes place slowly at constant gas temperature, allowing sufficient time for heat to be dissipated, then $T_1 = T_2 = T_3$.

The oil delivered to the circuit will be the difference between V_3 and V_2, and the pressure will drop to p_3 over this exchange period, hence p_3 has to be large enough that the circuit can continue to provide the forces needed.

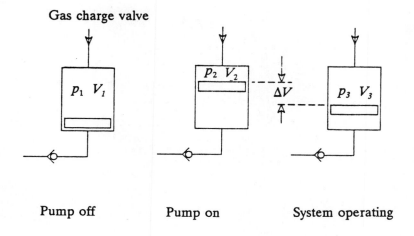

Figure 7.2 Volume Changes in an Accumulator

$$V_o = V_3 - V_2 = \frac{p_1 V_1}{p_3} - \frac{p_1 V_1}{p_2}$$

This corresponds to the oil volume delivered and therefore the accumulator size is given by:

$$V_1 = V_o \frac{\left(\dfrac{p_2}{p_1}\right)}{\left(\dfrac{p_2}{p_3} - 1\right)} \tag{7.1}$$

If, on the other hand, the gas is compressed or expanded rapidly, the heating or cooling generated causes pressure changes in addition to those occurring strictly as a result of volume change. This is because there is no heat transfer, and the following adiabatic equation must be used,

$$p_1 V_1^\gamma = p_2 V_2^\gamma = p_3 V_3^\gamma$$

$$V_o = V_3 - V_2 = \left(\frac{p_1 V_1^\gamma}{p_3}\right)^{\frac{1}{\gamma}} - \left(\frac{p_1 V_1^\gamma}{p_2}\right)^{\frac{1}{\gamma}}$$

$$= V_1\left(\left[\frac{p_1}{p_2}\right]^{\frac{1}{\gamma}} - \left[\frac{p_1}{p_2}\right]^{\frac{1}{\gamma}}\right)$$

(7.2)

In this case, the accumulator size is,

$$V_1 = \frac{\left(\frac{p_2}{p_1}\right)^{\frac{1}{\gamma}} V_o}{\left(\left[\frac{p_2}{p_3}\right]^{\frac{1}{\gamma}} - 1\right)}$$

(7.3)

The selection of precharge pressures depends on the application, and Table 7.1 summarizes some suggested guidelines.

For optimum service life, it is recommended that the volume change between fully charged and minimum working pressure should not be less than 20% or more than 80%.

In order to plot the behaviour of the gas volume (and hence the oil volume in an accumulator) between precharge pressure and any working pressure, equation (7.2) is written,

$$p_1 V_1^\gamma = p_w V_w^\gamma$$

where p_w and V_w are the conditions any pressure between p_2 and p_3.

Table 7.1

Purpose	Guideline
To supplement pump delivery	$p_1 = 90\%p_3$
To control, shock pressures	$p_1 = 60\%p_3$
As an emergency power source	$p_1 = p_3$
Reducing flow ripple	$p_1 = 70\%p_2$

$$V_w^{\gamma} = \frac{p_1 V_1^{\gamma}}{p_w}$$

$$\log V_w = \frac{1}{\gamma} \log\left(\frac{p_1 V_1^{\gamma}}{p_w}\right) \tag{7.4}$$

$$V_w = \text{antilog}\left(\frac{1}{\gamma} \log\left(\frac{p_1 V_1^{\gamma}}{p_w}\right)\right)$$

The oil volume at any pressure is then given by,

$$V_o = V_1 - V_w$$

Figure 7.3 shows some typical plots.

EXAMPLE 7.1

An accumulator has a precharge pressure of 900 kPa(g). Oil is slowly pumped in until the gas pressure increases to 2700 kPa(g). If the size of the accumulator is 0.4 m³, how much oil was pumped into it? If the accumulator was rapidly filled, what would be the new oil volume?

At precharge,

$$V_1 = 0.4 \text{ m}^3 \qquad\qquad p_1 = 900 + 101.3 = 1001.3 \text{ kPa}$$

At the end of the pumping process,

$$V_2 = ? \qquad\qquad p_2 = 2700 + 101.3 = 2801.3 \text{ kPa}$$

Since the filling is under isothermal conditions,

$$p_1 V_1 = p_2 V_2$$

$$V_2 = \frac{1001.3 \times 0.4}{2801.3} = 0.143 \text{ m}^3$$

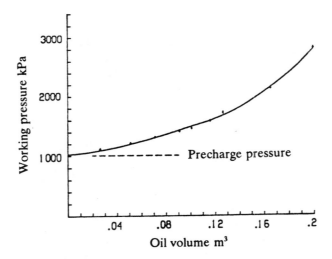

Figure 7.3 Accumulator Discharge Characteristics

But V_2 represents the new gas volume, hence the oil volume pumped in is,

$$V_o = V_1 - V_2 = 0.4 - 0.143 = 0.257 \text{ m}^3$$

Under rapid filling, adiabatic conditions exist, and if $\gamma = 1.4$,

$$V_2 = \left(\frac{p_1}{p_2}\right)^{\frac{1}{\gamma}} \times V$$

$$V_2 = \left(\frac{1001.3}{2801.3}\right)^{0.71} \times 0.4 = 0.1918 \text{ m}^3$$

$$V_o = 0.4 - 0.1918 = 0.208 \text{ m}^3$$

7.2 Supplemental flow

The accumulator can be used to supplement a pump in the circuit, where the duty cycle requires maximum power over a short period during the total cycle time. Rather than using a larger pump to satisfy this short period of high demand and therefore waste power, a small pump with a back-up accumulator can be used.

EXAMPLE 7.2

The circuit shown in Figure 7.4 includes an accumulator and an unload valve. After the accumulator has been charged, excess flow can then be dumped to the tank through this valve, since the valve's low-pressure loss does not waste power. The duty cycle for the system is shown in Figure 7.5, where it is seen that a high flow rate is required for only a short period of 3.0 s. It is more economical to provide this short-term demand using the accumulator, than to provide this flow continuously for a larger pump. Determine the optimum accumulator size, if the pump delivers 23.0 l/min at 20 MPa. The ram has a bore diameter of 160 mm and moves against a force of 267 kN on the outward stroke. The rod is required to travel 25.4 cm in 3.0 s. Assume losses are negligible.

The flow required over the 3.0 s period is,

$$Q = \frac{(160 \times 10^{-3})^2 \times 3.14}{4} \times \frac{25.4 \times 10^{-2}}{3} = 0.0017 \text{ m}^3/\text{s}$$

The minimum operating pressure to overcome the loading is,

$$p_L = \frac{267\,000}{0.02} = 13.35 \text{ MPa}$$

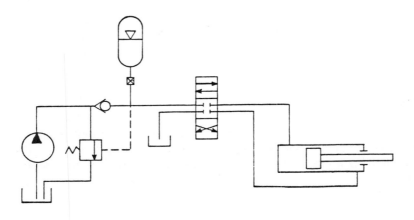

Figure 7.4 Circuit for Example 7.2

If a large pump were used, it would have to supply,

$$\text{Power} = 0.0017 \times 13.35 \times 10^6 = 22.69 \text{ kW}$$

at the ram.

However, the pump in use supplies only 23.0 l/min, and the supplemental flow needed is,

$$60 \times 0.0017 - 0.023 = 0.079 \text{ m}^3/\text{min}$$

The volume that needs to be supplied by the accumulator in 3.0 s is,

$$V = \frac{0.079 \times 3}{60} = 0.003\,95 \text{ m}^3$$

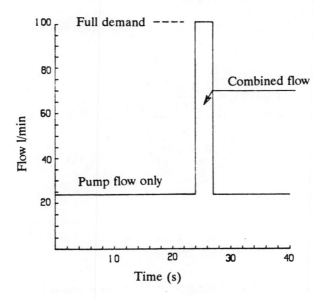

Figure 7.5 Flow Duty Cycle

Referring to Figure 7.5, the charging time for the accumulator is,

$$t = \frac{0.079 \times 3 \times 60}{23 \times 10^{-3} \times 60} = 10.3 \text{ s}$$

which is relatively long, and it is debatable whether to assume an isothermal or adiabatic condition; however the discharge time is 3.0 s. The relevant parameters are:

$$V_1 = \text{Accumulator size m}^3$$

$$V_o = \text{Required supplemental volume of oil} = 0.003\ 95\ \text{m}^3$$

$$p_1 = \text{Precharge pressure at 90\% of } p_3, \text{ (see Table 7.1)}$$

$$p_2 = \text{System pressure} = 20\ \text{MPa}$$

$$p_3 = \text{Minimum working pressure} = 13.35\ \text{MPa}$$

With pressures of this magnitude, correction to absolute values is not significant. For an adiabatic condition,

$$V_1 = \frac{0.003\ 95 \times \left(\dfrac{13.35 \times 10^6}{12.02 \times 10^6} \right)^{0.714}}{1 - \left(\dfrac{13.35 \times 10^6}{20 \times 10^6} \right)^{0.714}} = 0.016\ 97\ \text{m}^3$$

For isothermal conditions this value would be,

$$V_1 = 0.013\ 19\ \text{m}^3$$

In practice, the actual size of the accumulator chosen would be that nearest to a standard size.

7.3 Shock pulse control

If a valve in a fluid power circuit is suddenly closed, the fluid flow has kinetic energy which is rapidly changed into potential energy, causing a pressure pulse which would at least produce a lot of noise, or even cause a pipe or fitting failure.

When the fluid is stopped at the valve, a pressure wave then travels back up the pipe to the source at the speed of sound, for the particular liquid being used,

pipe to the source at the speed of sound, in the particular liquid being used,

$$c = \sqrt{\frac{N}{\rho}} \qquad (7.5)$$

The pressure wave will therefore take l/c s to propagate along the length l of the pipe. Such waves, in fact, travel up and down the pipe until the energy is dissipated.

$$\text{Kinetic Energy} = \frac{1}{2}m v^2 = \frac{1}{2}\rho l A \, v^2 \qquad (7.6)$$

$$\text{Potential Energy} = \frac{1}{2}\frac{l A}{N}p^2 \qquad (7.7)$$

The kinetic energy is a result of the flowing fluid, and the potential energy is due to the combined elasticity of the pipe and the oil contained in it acting like a spring. Hence, equating (7.6) and (7.7) results in,

$$p^2 = \rho N v^2$$

$$p = \sqrt{\frac{N}{\rho}}\sqrt{\rho^2 v} \qquad (7.8)$$

$$= (\rho c) v$$

In order to control this type of pressure build up, an accumulator is placed in the pipe at a distance l from the valve. Assume that prior to rapid closure of the valve, the gas volume in the accumulator is about 60% of the total gas volume V_w, as recommended in Table 7.1. The volume of oil that must be stored by the accumulator will be $V_w - V_2$ and is equal to the pump flow rate times the period it takes for the pressure wave to travel twice the length of the pipe,

$$V_w - V_2 = Q\frac{2l}{c}$$

Also from Boyle's Law,

$$p_w V_w^{\gamma} = p_2 V_2^{\gamma}$$

$$V_2 = V_w \left(\frac{p_w}{p_2} \right)^{\frac{1}{\gamma}}$$

$$V_w - V_w \left(\frac{p_w}{p_2} \right)^{\frac{1}{\gamma}} = Q \frac{2l}{c}$$

Now since $V_w = 0.6\,V_t$, where V_t is the size of the accumulator,

$$0.6\,V_t \left(1 - \left(\frac{p_w}{p_2} \right)^{\frac{1}{\gamma}} \right) = Q \frac{2l}{c}$$

$$V_t = \frac{3.33\,Ql}{c \left(1 - \left(\frac{p_w}{p_2} \right)^{\frac{1}{\gamma}} \right)}$$

(7.9)

EXAMPLE 7.3

A pump delivers flow to a pipe of length 13.65 m, at a rate of 1.89 l/s. A solenoid-operated valve at the end of the pipe is suddenly closed. If the pump supplies a pressure of 17.8 MPa, and the maximum pressure allowed to develop in the pipe is limited to 20.5 MPa, what size of accumulator is needed to protect the system?

First we need to determine the velocity of sound in hydraulic oil. Reasonable design values to use would be:

Density = 858.2 kg/m^3

Bulk modulus = 1.38 x 10^9 Pa

$$c = \sqrt{\frac{1.38 \times 10^9}{858.2}} = 1268.1 \ \text{m/s}$$

$$V_t = \frac{3.33 \times 1.89 \times 10^{-3} \times 13.65}{1268.1 \left[1 - \left(\dfrac{17.8 \times 10^6}{20.5 \times 10^6} \right)^{0.714} \right]} = 0.67 \times 10^{-3} \ \text{m}^3$$

7.4 Thermal expansion compensation

In a closed hydraulic circuit, an increase in temperature can cause fluid to expand. This will be compensated for to a small extent by the expansion of the pipework in the circuit, but the difference in expansion between the steel pipe and the contained oil, can still result in an increase in stress in the pipe.

The size of acculmulator to take care of thermal expansion can be calculated using,

$$V_1 = (\beta - 3\alpha)(T_2 - T_1) \times \frac{V_o \left(\dfrac{P_3}{P_1} \right)^{\frac{1}{\alpha}}}{1 - \left(\dfrac{P_3}{P_2} \right)^{\frac{1}{\alpha}}}$$

where:

    V_o is the total volume of fluid in the pipework (m^3)
    V_1 is the required size of accumulator (m^3)
    T_1 is the initial temperature of the oil (°C)
    T_2 is the final temperature of the oil (°C)
    α is the coefficient of linear expansion of the pipe (/ °C)
       (for steel pipe use 7 x 10^{-6}/ °C)
    β is the coefficient of volumetric expansion for oil (/ °C)
       (for hydraulic oil use 70 x 10^{-5}/ °C at 14 MPa)

7.5 Smoothing flow ripple

As was described in Chapter 6, it was shown that discrete packages of pressurized fluid are pumped into the delivery line. For precision hydraulic equipment, it is often required that this flow be smooth. In addition, ripple flow in the delivery line can excite pipe resonances and radiate noise. To solve these problems, an accumulator and a variable orifice can be used to create what is essentially the fluid power version of the electrical low pass filter.

One approach to this problem is to consider the analogous relationships between fluid power and electrical components. Flow rate Q, is analogous to electric current flow I, and fluid pressure p, is analogous to voltage V. However, linear analogies may only be applicable to a limited range of operation, because fluid power relationships are often non-linear. It is possible to construct fluid circuits analogous to electrical networks, starting from an understanding of electrical components that are analogous to basic fluid elements.

The three basic building blocks of electrical circuits are resistance, capacitance and inductance. The corresponding fluid power elements are respectively orifices or any flow restriction, fluid compressibility and the mass of fluid flowing in the circuit.

7.5.1 Fluid resistance

The effect of fluid resistance is characterized by a pressure drop in the direction of the flow. This is analogous to voltage drop across a resistance, more commonly known as Ohm's Law. For example, in the case of laminar flow in a pipe, the Hagen–Poiseuille formula (Chapter 8) stated,

$$\Delta p = \frac{128 \mu l Q}{\pi d^4} = R_h Q \qquad (7.10)$$

The units of hydraulic resistance R_h, are kg/m^4.s, called fluid ohms by some sources.

In the case of an orifice, the flow is turbulent,

$$Q = C_d a \sqrt{\frac{2 \Delta p}{\rho}}$$

so that,

$$\Delta p = \left(\frac{\rho}{2a^2 C_d^2}\right) Q^2 = R_h Q^2 \tag{7.11}$$

where R_h is now a non-linear resistance characteristic.

7.5.2 Fluid capacitance

Potential energy storage in a fluid can take the form of compression of the fluid, or it can be storage in the containing walls. A good example of fluid capacitance is the accumulator, while the hydraulic hose is a case where energy can be stored in the walls of the pipe. Compressibility of fluid was discussed in detail in Chapter 3,

$$\frac{dp}{dt} = \frac{N}{V} Q = \frac{1}{C_h} Q \tag{7.12}$$

The units of hydraulic capacitance C_h are $m^4 s^2/kg$, sometimes called fluid farads. Fluid capacitance can be determined experimentally by measuring the amount of fluid that must be slowly introduced into a pipe to produce a unit rise in pressure. Rapid introduction of the fluid would mean that inertia effects could not be ignored.

7.5.3 Fluid inertance

The analogy to electrical inductance is fluid inertance, which is a measure of the inertia forces developed when a fluid is accelerated in a pipe,

$$\Delta p = \frac{\rho l}{a} \frac{dQ}{dt} = L_h \frac{dQ}{dt} \tag{7.13}$$

The units of hydraulic inertance L_h are kg/m^4, called fluid henries by some sources. This parameter can be determined experimentally by measuring the rate of change of flow into a pipe, when a given pressure drop is slowly applied across the pipe length. If the pressure were applied too rapidly, then fluid capacitance would have to be taken into account.

7.5.4 Fluid impedance

In general, therefore, R_h, C_h and L_h can be termed the fluid impedances Z_h of a component or circuit, where,

$$p = Z_h Q \tag{7.14}$$

It is immediately apparent that both C_h and L_h are dependent on the rate of change of pressure and flow, respectively, with time. If the flow in the circuit is pulsating, or accelerating and decelerating, then these terms come into play. If the flow is steady, they play no part in the flow behaviour.

Another way of looking at these terms is to consider their behaviour in the frequency domain by letting $d/dt = \omega j$. Typical plots for capacitance and inductance against frequency are shown in Figure 7.6.

A simple model of a pulsation damper, is a pipe fitted with an accumulator on a tee and an adjustable orifice, as shown in Figure 7.7,

$$q = q_s + q_r = C_a \frac{dp}{dt} + \frac{p}{R_o}$$

$$R_o q_p = (C_a R_o s + 1)p$$

$$\frac{p}{q_p} = \frac{R_o}{1 + C_a R_o s} = \frac{R_o}{1 + Ts}$$

where T is the time constant, that is, the reciprocal of the break frequency of this simple low pass filter (see Chapter 2). Referring to Figure 7.8, if we set the break frequency $\omega_b < \omega_r$, the ripple frequency, we can get some attenuation due to the -6 dB/oct fall off of the amplitude response.

EXAMPLE 7.4

It is required to damp out a pressure peak which can be approximated to a rectangle pulse of 36 MPa, above the delivery pressure of 12 MPa, and lasts for 0.2 s. During this time the transient flow increased from the normal level of 0.0037–0.0148 m^3/s.

Find the size of accumulator that will reduce this peak to 20 MPa. Assume the series orifice R_o to have a fluid impedance of 54×10^8 Pa/m^3/s.

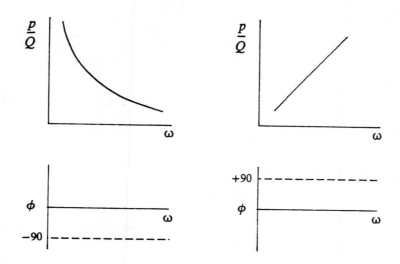

Figure 7.6 Impedance Characteristics

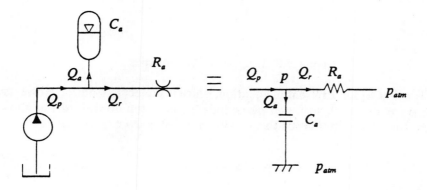

Figure 7.7 Circuit for Example 7.4

This circuit is similar to Figure 7.7 and so if q_s is the input flow in Figure 7.9, then,

$$q_s = q_a + q_r$$

$$R_o q_s = p + T \frac{dp}{dt}$$

where $T = R_o C_a$.

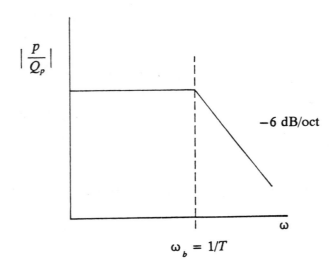

Figure 7.8 Damper Characteristics

This is a first-order differential equation, which is subject to a pulse. However, the pulse starts at $t = 0$, so it can be considered as a step downwards, as shown in Figure 7.8. The solution for this condition is well known,

$$p = R_o q \left(1 - e^{-\frac{t}{T}}\right)$$

where,

p = The allowable value of pressure above steady state

= 36 − 12 = 12 MPa

q = The allowable value of flow above steady state

= 0.0148 − 0.0037 = 0.0111 m³/s

Substitute these values into the solution of the equation,

$$24 \times 10^6 = 0.011 \times 54 \times 10^8 \left(1 - e^{\frac{-0.2}{T}}\right)$$

$$0.404 = 1 - e^{\frac{-0.2}{T}}$$

$$\log_e 0.404 = -0.906 = -\frac{0.2}{T}$$

$$T = R_o C_a = 0.221 \text{ s}$$

$$C_a = \frac{0.221}{54 \times 10^8} = 4.088 \times 10^{-11} \text{ m}^3/\text{Pa}$$

The value for the capacitance C_a, represents the size the accumulator needs to be for each Pascal of pressure. In this case, the pressure is 24 MPa, therefore,

Accumulator size = $4.088 \times 10^{-11} \times 24 \times 10^6 = 0.98 \times 10^{-3}$ m³

The plot of the way the pressure is expected to behave, with and without the accumulator installed is shown in Figure 7.10.

EXAMPLE 7.5

Compare the natural frequencies, if a steel pipe 2.5 m long in a circuit is replaced by a hydraulic hose of the same length. The pipes have an internal diameter of 10 mm NB, and the bulk modulus of oil filled hose to be 350 MPa. Assume the modulus of steel as 210 GPa, the density of oil as 858.2 kg/m³. If the viscosity of the oil is 0.034 Pa.s, calculate the damping ratio for each case.

A pipe filled with oil can be thought of as a spring mass damper, and is therefore represented by a second-order differential equation. The representation is shown in Figure 7.11.

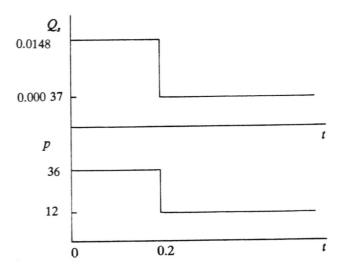

Figure 7.9 Pressure and Flow Plots

First, obtain an expression for the input and output impedances for the pipe using well established electrical methods,

$$\frac{P_u}{Q_u} = R_h + L_h s + \frac{1}{C_h s}$$

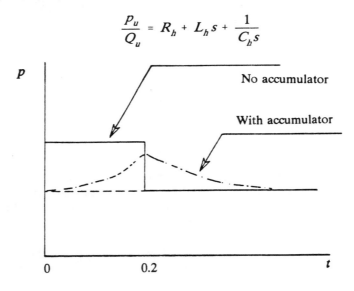

Figure 7.10 Circuit Performance

and,

$$\frac{P_d}{Q_d} = \frac{1}{C_h s}$$

If it is assumed that $Q_u = Q_d$ for this pipe section, then the relationship between the upstream and downstream pressures will be,

$$\frac{P_d}{P_u} = \frac{1}{L_h C_h s^2 + R_h C_h s + 1}$$

$$= \frac{1}{\dfrac{1}{\omega_n^2} s^2 + \dfrac{2\xi}{\omega_n} s + 1}$$

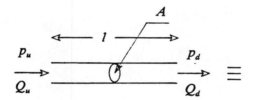

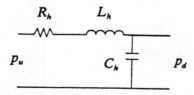

Figure 7.11 Pipe Model

By comparison therefore,

$$\omega_n = \frac{1}{\sqrt{L_h C_h}} \qquad \xi = \frac{R_h}{2}\sqrt{\frac{c_h}{L_h}}$$

For the steel pipe filled with oil,

$$N_{steel} = \frac{tE}{d} = \frac{2.3 \times 210 \times 10^9}{17.1} = 28.24 \text{ GPa}$$

since schedule 40, 10 mm NB, seamless steel pipe has an actual internal diameter of 12.5 mm and outside diameter of 17.1 mm.

Assume that the pipe is filled with hydraulic oil of bulk modulus 12×10^8 Pa. The effective bulk modulus is based on the fact that the oil and the pipe wall are two springs in series,

$$\frac{1}{N_e} = \frac{1}{28.24 \times 10^9} + \frac{1}{1.2 \times 10^9}$$

$$N_e = 1.151 \times 10^9 \text{ Pa}$$

The equivalent capacitance of the oil filled steel pipe is,

$$C_h = \frac{V}{N} = A\frac{l}{N} = \frac{12.23 \times 10^{-5} \times 2.5}{1.151 \times 10^9} = 2.664 \times 10^{-13} \text{ m}^4\text{s}^2/\text{kg}$$

The equivalent capacitance of the oil filled hose,

$$C_h = \frac{12.26 \times 10^{-5} \times 2.5}{0.35 \times 10^9} = 8.757 \times 10^{-13} \text{ m}^4\text{s}^2/\text{kg}$$

The equivalent inductance for both pipes,

$$L_h = \frac{\rho l}{A} = \frac{858.2 \times 2.5}{12.26 \times 10^{-5}} = 1.75 \times 10^7 \text{ kg/m}^4$$

Assuming laminar flow for both pipes,

$$R_h = \frac{128 \mu l}{\pi d^4} = \frac{128 \times 0.034 \times 2.5}{3.14 \times (12.5 \times 10^{-3})^4} = 1.43 \times 10^8 \text{ kg/m}^4\text{s}$$

For the steel pipe,

$$f_n = \frac{1}{2\pi} \sqrt{\frac{1}{1.75 \times 10^7 \times 2.664 \times 10^{-13}}} = 74.08 \text{ Hz}$$

$$\zeta = \frac{1.43 \times 10^8}{2} \frac{\sqrt{2.664 \times 10^{-13}}}{1.75 \times 10^7} = 0.009$$

For the hydraulic hose,

$$f_n = \frac{1}{2\pi} \sqrt{\frac{1}{1.75 \times 10^7 \times 8.757 \times 10^{-13}}} = 40.68 \text{ Hz}$$

$$\zeta = \frac{1.43 \times 10^8}{2} \sqrt{\frac{8.757 \times 10^{-13}}{1.75 \times 10^7}} = 0.016$$

In the case of the hose, the damping will be higher still, due to the natural damping of the rubber.

The following points should be noted with respect to this example:

- Pipes can act as accumulators, since they are capable of storing energy under pressure.

- The model considered in the example above assumes lumped parameters, and therefore only exhibits a fundamental natural frequency. In fact the mass, damping, and stiffness are distributed throughout the pipe length and therefore in practice there are many modes of resonance.

 - While the hydraulic hose will reduce the radiation of noise due to its higher damping characteristics than steel pipe, the fact that the stiffness is lower can effect the response of the system.

 - Particularly with steel piping, when the passive natural frequency nears 60 Hz or a multiple of it, the pipe can be set in motion due to vibrational energy from the pump or electric motor.

EXERCISES

7.1. A system is required to deliver 0.8×10^{-3} m^3 of oil over a period of 0.2 s with a minimum time between demands of 28 s. Determine the necessary accumulator size, if the pump associated with the system has a delivery of 0.25×10^{-3} m^3/s and a maximum delivery pressure of 7.5 MPa. The minimum working pressure is 1.0 MPa. What capacity pump would be required for this system, if no accumulator were included?

7.2. A hydraulic circuit using an accumulator is required to supply 2×10^{-3} m^3/s over a period of 2.0 s at the end of a 20 s cycle of operation. Over the normal part of the cycle the flow is 0.5×10^{-3} m^3/s, and this period is used to recharge the accumulator. If the supply pressure is 25 MPa and the minimum working pressure is 12 MPa, calculate the size of accumulator required. What is the value of the power required from the pump, with and without the accumulator?

7.3. An accumulator, having a total volume of 4.92×10^{-3} m^3, is charged with nitrogen to 6.89 MPa. After settling down at a temperature of 37.8°C, the oil side is slowly pressurized with oil at 20.67 MPa. Some time later a rapid demand of 14.76×10^{-3} m^3/min is made for 3.0 s. What will be the gas temperature at the end of the 3.0 s period? How much work has been done?

7.4. A hydraulic moulding press for rubber products has a cylinder piston diameter of 2.3 mm, and is required to generate a load of 498 176 N. The required ram travel is 13 cm over a period of 1.5 s. The curing time for the rubber is 2 min and another 2 min is required for the operator to remove the work and reload the press for the next cycle. What is the required pump flow rate, and power? If a pump of 3.4×10^{-3} m^3/min flow rate and 20.7 MPa supply pressure is now selected, what accumulator size is needed to provide supplemental flow?

7.5. A pump has a single piston of diameter 10.16 cm, and a stroke of 25.4 cm. The pumping action causes the pressure in the delivery line to oscillate unacceptably about the design operating pressure of 20.67 MPa. This results in excessive noise being radiated. Determine the size of accumulator that would limit the pressure fluctuations to ±5% of the operating pressure.

7.6. An accumulator is attached to a pump set and slowly charged until the oil pressure is 25 MPa. The temperature is allowed to settle at 24°C. The accumulator has an initial gas charge of 10.5 MPa and a volume of 5×10^{-5} m^3 prior to the oil being pumped in. A valve is then operated which shuts off the pump set and allows the pressurized oil to enter a hydraulic motor, until the oil in the accumulator is spent. If the displacement of the motor is 1.5×10^{-5} m^3/rev, how many turns will the shaft of the motor rotate? What was the oil pressure at the time when the oil was just spent? How much work has been expended?

7.7. A seven piston pump has the following parameters:

Speed	1800 rpm
Output flow	0.378 l/s
Ripple flow	5% of output flow

The pump feeds a pipe 10 mm NB and 0.5 m long, with a restrictance at the end. Determine:

(a) The fluid inductance of the pipe.
(b) The peak ripple pressure based on the inductive component only.
(c) Compare the resistive impedance of the line with the inductive impedance for the pump speed of 1800 rpm.
(d) If the pump is assumed to have a volumetric efficiency of 95% and an overall efficiency of 92%, calculate the pump displacement, output power, input shaft power, and pump shaft torque.

CHAPTER 8

Circuit design

8.1 Introduction

A fluid power circuit is designed by connecting the basic building blocks, that is, components with piping. Usually a specification is given for the required performance, defining the output power and loading requirements. The major objective is then to select the pipe sizes, components and input power requirement that will meet the performance. The difference between the input and output power will be the losses in the circuit. At the same time, the cost of the system has to be optimized.

The major portion of the energy lost is converted into heat, and a small amount into noise. Noise still manages to create a major annoyance and sometimes a health hazard. While noise can do damage to the human operator, heat does damage to the equipment if it is not dissipated efficiently.

In attempting to calculate these losses, some parameters can be determined with acceptable precision, some values remain constant, and others are very difficult to evaluate. For example, the cross-sectional area of a pipe is easily calculated, but a value for seal friction can only be a guess. Circuit design is therefore in many respects an art, relying on experience and to some extent an iterative process.

8.2 Kirchhoff's laws applied to fluid power circuits

It is convenient to borrow two fundamental principles from electrical circuit design, since within certain constraints, pressure can be considered as analogous to voltage and flow to current.

(a) The first law (Figure 8.1a) states that the algebraic sum of pressure drops around a closed circuit must be zero.

(b) The second law (Figure 8.1b) states that the algebraic sum of the flows entering a junction and leaving it must also be zero.

In the first law, the flow is common and the pressure changes, but in the second law the pressure is common and the flow changes through the circuit. From Figure 8.1a,

$$P_s - P_{atm} = (P_s - P_1) + (P_1 - P_2) + (P_2 - P_{atm}) \qquad (8.1)$$

and for Figure 8.1b,

Power into the junction = Power out of the junction

$$Q_1 P + Q_2 P = Q_3 P + Q_4 P + Q_5 P$$

$$Q_1 + Q_2 = Q_3 + Q_4 + Q_5 \qquad (8.2)$$

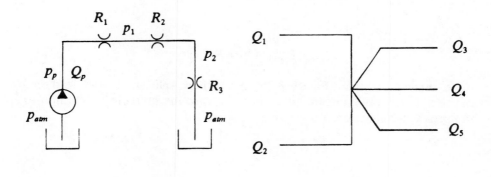

(a) Pressure law   (b) Flow law

Figure 8.1a,b Kirchhoff's Laws for Circuits

For example, some typical configurations are shown in Figures 8.2 a,b,c. The first diagram (Figure 8.2a) shows components in series, and hence this is termed a series circuit, where,

$$Q_1 = Q_2 = Q_3$$

$$P_s - P_{atm} = (P_s - P_1) + (P_1 - P_2) + (P_2 - P_{atm})$$

(8.3)

Since the pressures are usually measured as gauge, $p_{atm} = 0$.

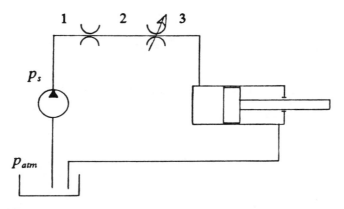

Figure 8.2a. Open Series

The second diagram (Figure 8.2b) has a flow split in it, and is therefore classified as a parallel circuit, because in this case the pressure is common to all the pipes at the junction,

$$Q_1 = Q_2 + Q_3$$

$$P_1 = P_2 = P_3$$

(8.4)

The resistance to flow can be the result of an orifice or a variable area within a valve, a leakage path or just the resistance to flow offered by a length of pipe or a fitting. An example of a closed parallel circuit is show in (Figure 8.2c).

Because of the analogy to electrical circuits, the relationship between pressure and flow can be considered as the Ohm's Law for fluid flow,

$$\Delta p = R_h Q$$

(8.5)

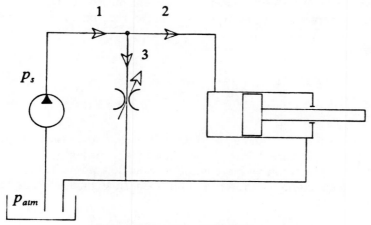

Figure 8.2b Open Parallel

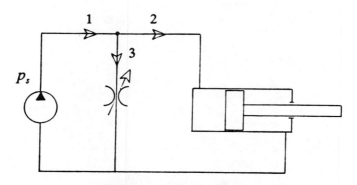

Figure 8.2c Closed Parallel

The fluid resistance relationships were developed in Chapter 7, hence for laminar flow condition equation (7.10),

$$\Delta p = \frac{128\mu l}{\pi d^4}Q = R_h Q \tag{8.6}$$

In this case, the value can be exactly calculated, but for turbulent flow in an orifice, the discharge coefficient must be obtained experimentally.

Referring to equation (7.11),

$$\Delta p = \frac{\rho}{2(aC_d)^2} Q^2 = R_h Q^2 \tag{8.7}$$

The resistance to flow, R_h, can be an orifice, a leakage path, a variable area valve, or just the loss of pressure due to friction in a pipe or fitting.

A network of restrictors can be replaced by a single equivalent value, so in the case of a series circuit, in the presence of turbulent flow, Figure 8.3, and since the flows are common,

$$\Delta p = \Delta p_1 + \Delta p_2 + \Delta p_3$$

$$R_T Q^2 = R_1 Q^2 + R_2 Q^2 + R_3 Q^2 \tag{8.8}$$

$$R_T = R_1 + R_2 + R_3 \tag{8.9}$$

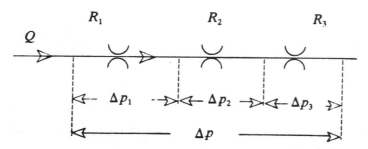

Figure 8.3. Orifices in Series

If the restrictors are now in parallel, Figure 8.4, then,

$$Q = Q_1 + Q_2 + Q_3$$

$$Q = \sqrt{\frac{\Delta p_1}{R_1}} + \sqrt{\frac{\Delta p_2}{R_2}} + \sqrt{\frac{\Delta p_3}{R_3}} \qquad (8.10)$$

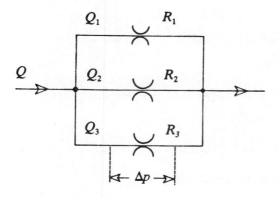

Figure 8.4 Orifices in Parallel

But since,

$$\Delta p_1 = \Delta p_2 = \Delta p_3 = \Delta p$$

then,

$$\frac{1}{\sqrt{R}} = \frac{1}{\sqrt{R_1}} + \frac{1}{\sqrt{R_2}} + \frac{1}{\sqrt{R_3}} \qquad (8.11)$$

A circuit which contains both series and parallel elements is shown in Figure 8.5, for the parallel part of the circuit,

$$\frac{1}{\sqrt{R_{23}}} = \frac{1}{\sqrt{R_2}} + \frac{1}{\sqrt{R_3}} = \frac{\sqrt{R_3} + \sqrt{R_2}}{\sqrt{R_2 R_3}}$$

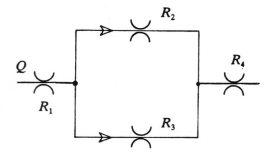

Figure 8.5 Orifices in Combination

Hence the equivalent series resistance is,

$$R_{23} = \frac{R_2 R_3}{R_2 + R_3 + 2\sqrt{R_2 R_3}}$$

The new equivalent series circuit is shown in Figure 8.6, and the total restrictance will be given by,

$$R_T = R_1 + R_2 + R_3$$

$$= (R_1 + R_4) + \frac{R_2 R_3}{R_2 + R_3 + 2\sqrt{R_2 R_3}}$$

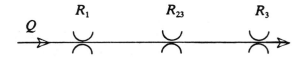

Figure 8.6 Equivalent Orifices in Series

A more complicated situation is where the restrictances are connected in the equivalent of a Wheatstone Bridge arrangement, like that shown in Figure 8.7. One approach is to use the Hardy-Cross method [16], which is based on Newton's method of finding zeros of a function.

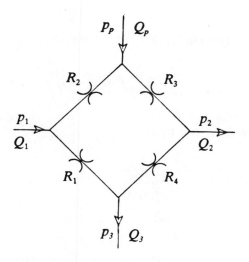

Figure 8.7 Equivalent Bridge Circuit

Referring to Figure 8.7, the flow continuity gives,

$$Q_p + Q_1 = Q_2 + Q_3$$

Applying Kirchhoff's Laws, the algebraic sum of the pressure drops around the circuit must be zero. The approach is to guess the flow distribution in each pipe and work out the error of the guess, then repeat the process until Kirchhoff's Law is satisfied with an acceptable error. If the value of the flow through each restrictance is estimated within an error ϵ, then since the sum of the pressure drops must be zero,

$$\sum R (Q + \epsilon)^2 = 0 \qquad\qquad (8.12)$$

where Q is the accurate flow value through each restrictance.
Expanding equation (8.12),

$$\sum R\,Q^2 + 2\sum R\,Q\epsilon + \sum R\,\epsilon^2 = 0$$

If ϵ is small compared to Q, then $R\epsilon^2 \approx 0$, and therefore,

$$\sum R\,Q^2 + 2\sum R\,Q\epsilon = 0$$

so that the error can be estimated from,

$$\epsilon = -\frac{\sum RQ^2}{2\sum RQ} \tag{8.13}$$

or in general,

$$\epsilon = -\frac{\sum RQ^n}{n\sum RQ^{n-1}} \tag{8.14}$$

The following procedure should be noted in using this error evaluation:

1. Some direction for each loop of the network must be chosen as positive for a given pressure gradient, for example clockwise direction of flow (positive) for reducing pressure.

2. To ensure the correct sign for the pressure gradient, RQ^2, should be written as $R|Q|Q$.

3. A complex system is divided up into a number of meshes N and a correction is found for each. The minimum number of meshes M necessary for a complete solution is given by $M = N - J + 1$, where J is the number of junctions.

EXAMPLE 8.1

A circuit consists of a pump moving oil through the circuit shown in Figure 8.8. The pressure at the pump outlet is 7 MPa, and at p_3. it has dropped to 4.8 MPa. Assuming turbulent flow, values for the restrictors are,

$$R_1 = 5.43 \times 10^{11} \qquad\qquad R_2 = 10.33 \times 10^{11}$$

$$R_3 = 17.76 \times 10^{11} \qquad\qquad R_4 = 33.0 \times 10^{11}$$

What is the value for the flow rate Q_p out of the pump? What is the flow rate through restrictor R_4? What is the orifice area of R_2?

Since the flow is turbulent, then equation (8.7) is used, and referring to equation 6.11, it is seen that,

$$R_h = \frac{1}{3.12 \times 10^{-2}\, a^2}$$

where a is the orifice area in metres.

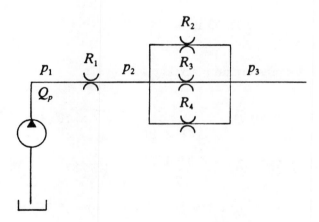

Figure 8.8 Circuit for Example 8.1

To find Q_p, first determine the total equivalent restrictance of the circuit. For the parallel section,

$$\frac{1}{\sqrt{R_{234}}} = \frac{1}{\sqrt{R_2}} + \frac{1}{\sqrt{R_3}} + \frac{1}{\sqrt{R_3}}$$

$$= 0.984 \times 10^{-6} + 0.75 \times 10^{-6} + 0.55 \times 10^{-6}$$

$$\frac{1}{\sqrt{R_{234}}} = 2.284 \times 10^{-6}$$

$$R_{234} = 1.917 \times 10^{11}$$

The total series resistance is now,

$$R_T = 5.43 \times 10^{11} + 1.917 \times 10^{11} = 7.347 \times 10^{11}$$

and the flow from the pump must be,

$$Q_p = \frac{1}{\sqrt{7.347 \times 10^{11}}} \times \sqrt{(7 - 4.8) \times 10^6}$$

$$= 0.001\ 73\ \text{m}^3/\text{s}$$

Now determine the pressure drop across p_1,

$$0.001\ 73 = \frac{1}{\sqrt{5.43 \times 10^{11}}} \times \sqrt{7 \times 10^6 - p_2}$$

$$\sqrt{7 \times 10^6 - p_2} = \frac{0.001\ 73}{0.1357 \times 10^{-5}} = 1275.87$$

$$p_2 = 7 \times 10^6 - 1.63 \times 10^6 = 5.37\ \text{MPa}$$

The flow through restrictor R is,

$$Q_4 = \frac{1}{\sqrt{33 \times 10^{11}}} \times \sqrt{(5.37 - 4.8) \times 10^6}$$

$$= 0.000\,42 \text{ m}^3/\text{s}$$

The diameter of the R_2 is,

$$R_2 = 10.33 \times 10^{11} = \frac{1}{(3.12 \times 10^{-2} \times a)^2}$$

$$3.12 \times 10^{-2} \times a = 0.984 \times 10^{-6}$$

$$a = 0.000\,032 \text{ m}^2$$

$$d = 6.338 \text{ mm}$$

EXAMPLE 8.2

A circuit consisting of five restrictors is arranged as shown in Figure 8.9. The values of the restrictors are:

$$R_1 = 15 \times 10^{11}, \qquad R_2 = 13 \times 10^{11}$$

$$R_3 = 12 \times 10^{11}, \qquad R_4 = 7 \times 10^{11}$$

$$R_5 = 5 \times 10^{11}$$

If the flow Q_p from the pump is 0.002 m³/s, find the flow through each restrictor.

The first step is to make a rough guess at what the flow might be in each pipe. Since,

$$Q = \sqrt{\frac{\Delta p}{R_h}}$$

then the larger the value of R_h, the smaller the flow, so we can make some estimates using this fact.

The smallest flow will be through R_1, and the largest through R_5. Also the main flow Q_p splits into $Q1$ and $Q4$,

$$\frac{Q_1}{Q_4} = \sqrt{\frac{R_4}{R_1}} = \sqrt{\frac{7}{15}} = 0.683$$

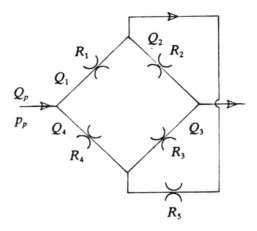

Figure 8.9 Bridge Circuit for Example 8.2

If the flow into the network is,

$$Q_p = Q_1 + Q_4 = Q_1 + \frac{Q_1}{0.683} = 0.002$$

Therefore,

$$Q_1 = \frac{0.002}{1 + 1.4641} = 0.812 \times 10^{-3}$$

$$Q_4 = 1.188 \times 10^{-3}$$

At the next junction, we know the value of Q_1.

$$0.812 \times 10^{-3} = Q_2 + Q_5$$

$$\frac{Q_2}{Q_5} = \sqrt{\frac{5}{10}} = 0.707$$

therefore,

$$0.812 \times 10^{-3} = Q_2 + \frac{Q_2}{0.707} = 2.4144 \, Q_2$$

$$Q_2 = 0.3363 \times 10^{-3}$$

$$Q_5 = 0.4757 \times 10^{-3}$$

Loop 1 consists of $+Q_1$, $+Q_5$ and $-Q_4$, the error can now be estimated,

$$\epsilon_{L1} = \frac{-[15 \times 0.812^2 + 5 \times 0.475^2 - 7 \times 1.18^2] \times 10^{-3}}{2 \times [15 \times 0.812 + 5 \times 0.475 - 7 \times 1.18]}$$

$$= \frac{-1.275 \times 10^{-3}}{2 \times 6.295} = -1.0127 \times 10^{-4}$$

This error correction is applied to each of the estimated flow values in the loop. The new flow values are,

$$Q_1 = 0.812 \times 10^{-3} - 1.0127 \times 10^{-4} = 0.711 \times 10^{-3}$$

$$Q_4 = 1.880 \times 10^{-3} - 1.0127 \times 10^{-4} = 1.779 \times 10^{-3}$$

$$Q_5 = 0.476 \times 10^{-3} - 1.0127 \times 10^{-4} = 0.374 \times 10^{-3}$$

These values are then used for a further assessment of error and the process repeated until an acceptable accuracy is obtained.

8.3 Pipeline design

For the selection of pipe for hydraulic circuits, it is generally recommended that:

(a) Suction lines to pumps should be sized so that the fluid velocity does not exceed 1.2 m/s. This is to ensure minimum pressure loss and to help prevent cavitation at the inlet side of the pump.

(b) Delivery lines should be sized so that the fluid velocity does not exceed 4.5 m/s. This is to prevent shock loading on rapid valve closure. When fluid flowing in a pipe is suddenly stopped by, say, a rapidly closing valve, a large pressure transient may result. The fluid adjacent to the valve is blocked and a pressure wave travels back to the fluid source at a velocity c, such that,

$$c = \sqrt{\frac{N}{\rho}}$$

where c is the velocity of sound in the fluid. When the pressure wave arrives at the source, in l/c s, l being the length of the pipe, the kinetic energy of the moving mass of fluid will be stored as potential energy in the fluid and the elastic walls of the pipe. At this stage the pressure of the compressed fluid is at a maximum and a decompression wave forms and travels back to the closed valve. These waves continue to propagate with an associated interchange between kinetic and potential of energies, until friction effects eventually destroy the energy.

$$\text{Kinetic Energy} = \frac{1}{2}\rho\, la v^2$$

$$\text{Potential Energy} = \frac{1}{2}\frac{la}{N}\, p^2 = \frac{1}{2}\frac{la}{\rho c^2}\, p^2$$

$$p = (\rho c)\, v$$

$$p = 858.2 \times 1268 \times 4.5 = 5.0 \text{ MPa}$$

Hence, at the recommended flow velocity of 4.5 m/s, the pressure in the pipe should not exceed 5.0 MPa, plus the normal working pressure in the pipe.

(c) Return lines should be a size larger than delivery lines to minimize back-pressure effects. Unfortunately in most circuits, delivery and return line reverse rolls under the control of the directional control valve, and end up the same size.

Table 8.1 shows the generally accepted guidelines for pipe diameter selection. For calculation purposes, the nominal bore (NB) dimensions are not necessarily the same as those used for calculations. Table 8.2 shows the outside (OD) and inside (ID) diameters for schedule 40 hydraulic piping used for general industrial hydraulic systems. Gas, water or copper pipe and fittings should never be used for hydraulic circuits.

Schedule sizes refer to the wall thickness; the higher the schedule number, the thicker the wall. Schedule 40 is termed standard pipe, so 10 mm NB pipe has a wall thickness of 4.6 mm, schedule 80, extra heavy, has a wall thickness of 6.4 mm for the same size of pipe. Notice that in these schedule sizes the OD remains the same, and the ID gets smaller. The required ID is based on the flow rate, but the OD is based on the loading, especially exposure to mechanical vibration or fluid shock loads. The burst pressure of piping can be calculated from,

$$\text{Burst Pressure} = \frac{2t\,s}{OD}$$

where t is the wall thickness and s the radial tensile strength (517 MPa). Table 8.2 shows allowable working pressure based on 1/3 of the burst pressure.
It is possible to lower the cost of pipework by pipe bending, as opposed to using fittings; however, it is important not to make the bend radius too small as it can result in damage to the pipe. The radius of a tube bend should not be less then three times the tube OD.

8.4 Pressure losses in piping

It is usual to size pipe work so as to minimize pressure loss and to keep the flow laminar where possible to reduce noise. For the purposes of design, it is assumed that laminar flow exists if the Reynolds number is less than 2000.

Table 8.1

Flow Rate		Suction	Delivery	Return
ml/s	m³/s	mm(NB)	mm(NB)	mm(NB)
150	1.5×10^{-4}	15	8	10
300	3.0×10^{-4}	20	10	15
530	5.3×10^{-4}	20	15	20
1280	12.8×10^{-4}	32	20	25
1890	18.9×10^{-4}	40	25	32
3000	30.0×10^{-4}	50	32	40
5300	53.0×10^{-4}	65	40	50

Table 8.2

Nominal Bore (mm)	Outside Dia. (mm)	Inside Dia. (mm)	Allowable Working MPa
8	13.7	9.2	46.4
10	17.1	12.5	38.4
15	21.3	15.8	36.9
20	26.7	20.9	30.6
25	33.4	26.6	28.8
32	42.2	35.1	24.0
40	48.3	40.9	21.7
50	60.3	52.5	18.4

The pressure losses in hydraulic pipe can be estimated using the Darcy formula,

$$\Delta p = \frac{fl}{d} \frac{\rho v^2}{2} = K \frac{\rho v^2}{2} \qquad (8.15)$$

where K is termed the loss coefficient, f the friction factor, l the pipe section length, d the diameter and v the average flow velocity. The friction factor has been shown experimentally to be a function of Reynolds number and pipe internal roughness [17]. However for design purposes the following can be used. For laminar flow conditions it is found that,

$$f = \frac{64}{Re} \qquad (8.16)$$

By substituting into equation (8.15),

$$\Delta p = \frac{64}{Re} \frac{l\rho}{2d} V^2$$

But,

$$Re = \rho \frac{dv}{\mu}$$

$$\Delta p = \frac{64 \, \mu l}{2d^2} v$$

and for a pipe with a circular cross-section,

$$Q = \frac{\pi d^2}{4} v$$

$$\Delta p = \frac{128 \, \mu l}{\pi d^4} Q \qquad (8.17)$$

This is known as the Hagen–Poiseuille formula for laminar pipe flow, but should not be confused with equation (3.5) for leakage flow through a narrow passage.

In the case of turbulent flow, the friction factor can be approximated using the Blasius formula,

$$f = \frac{0.316}{Re^{0.25}}$$

so that,

$$\Delta p = \frac{0.316}{Re^{0.25}} \frac{l\rho}{2d} v^2$$

For convenience, Table 8.3 and a four-step procedure has been prepared for calculating pipe losses,

To calculate the pressure drop across a pipe of length l in which industrial hydraulic oil is flowing of density 858.2 kg/m³, the steps are:

1. From Table 8.2, select the required pipe diameter. Then using Table 8.3, find the value for K_1, which is simply $4/\pi d$. This allows the Reynolds number to be estimated,

$$Re = \frac{K_1 Q}{v}$$

$$v = 4.0 \times 10^{-5} \text{ m}^2/\text{s}$$

   if a value for viscosity is not known at the stage of the design.

2. From the value of Re, decide if the flow is laminar or turbulent. Then calculate the friction factor using,

$$Re < 2000 \qquad f = \frac{64}{Re}$$

$$Re > 2000 \qquad f = \frac{0.316}{Re^{0.25}}$$

3. Based on the selected pipe diameter, select the appropriate value for K_2, from Table 8.3. K_2 is simply $2A^2/\rho$.

4. The pressure drop across the pipe is then,

$$\Delta p = \frac{fl}{d} \frac{Q^2}{k_2}$$

$$= \frac{K}{K_2} Q^2$$

where K is the loss coefficient, fl/d.

Table 8.3

Nominal Bore (mm)	K_1	K_2	Cross-section Area (m²)
8	138	1.027×10^{-11}	6.64×10^{-5}
10	102	3.506×10^{-11}	12.27×10^{-5}
15	81	8.949×10^{-11}	19.60×10^{-5}
20	61	2.740×10^{-10}	34.30×10^{-5}
25	47	7.195×10^{-10}	55.57×10^{-5}
32	36	2.818×10^{-9}	96.76×10^{-5}
40	31	4.014×10^{-9}	13.13×10^{-4}
50	24	1.090×10^{-8}	21.64×10^{-4}

Unfortunately not all piping is in straight runs so when a bend occurs, the loss of pressure will be greater. The effective bend loss can be estimated from an equivalent length of standard pipe. A similar approach can be used for fittings, valves and other components.

Equation (8.15) shows that the pressure loss in a pipe section is proportional to the length of the pipe, as well as the flow velocity squared. On the other hand, experimental tests carried on a range of fittings, valves and other components, show that the pressure loss is also proportional to the fluid velocity squared, but no length is involved, so that,

$$p = \frac{K\rho}{2} v^2 \tag{8.18}$$

where K is the loss factor for the fitting involved. Some examples of K values are shown in Table 8.4.

Table 8.4

Component (NB)		15 mm	20 mm	25 mm	32 mm
Globe Valve	open	9.50	8.70	7.90	7.25
	50% open	12.50	11.40	10.39	9.54
Gate Valve	open	0.36	0.33	0.30	0.275
	50% open	4.50	4.125	3.75	3.44
Tee		1.70	1.55	1.40	1.3
90° Bend		0.82	0.75	0.68	0.63
45° Bend		0.43	0.395	0.36	0.33
Filter (25 μm)		4.00	4.0	4.00	4.0

Information regarding K factors for hydraulic equipment is quite difficult to obtain, and often you have to carry out your own pressure–flow tests on particular component types. The best information is in papers by J.D. Hamilton *et al.* [18,19]. The relationships for losses in pipes, and in fittings, suggests that there is an equivalent length of pipe that would give a similar pressure loss to the actual fitting. Equating equations (8.15) and (8.18) gives,

$$\frac{f\rho}{2d} l v^2 = \frac{K\rho}{2} v^2$$

$$l_{eqv} = \frac{Kd}{f} = \frac{KdRe}{64}$$

Hence using Table 8.4, a 20 mm (NB) tee has a $K = 1.55$; then, if the flow is assumed laminar at $Re = 1500$,

$$l_{eqv} = \frac{1.55 \times 20.9 \times 1500}{64 \times 10} = 75.93 \text{ cm}$$

and for calculation purposes, this tee can be replaced with 75.93 cm of straight pipe.

Sudden contractions and enlargements occur where a pipe is attached to an actuating cylinder, pump or reservoir. The loss coefficient can be estimated from Figure 8.10.

Loss coefficients for directional control valves will vary, depending on the manufacturer, since the way the internal passage ways are arranged will affect these values. A typical set of results is shown in Table 8.5. Notice for example that the pressure loss is greater for flow going from the B ram port to the tank, than it is for flow going from the inlet pressure port to the tank.

Table 8.5

Re	P-T	P-A or P-B	A-T	B-T
0500	40	55	53	60
1000	28	40	40	48
1500	25	32	35	43
2000	22	29	32	40
3000	19	25	30	40
5000	17	22	29	40

EXAMPLE 8.3

A simple hydraulic circuit, as shown in Figure 8.11, consists of a pump set, directional control valve and a ram, to produce controlled mechanical power. Figure 8.12 shows the physical dimensions of the pipework and components. The required specification for performance is:

Pump:
A gear pump was selected, mainly on the basis of its low cost. Rated delivery is 1.0×10^{-3} m³/s. The working pressure is to be selected on optimal power useage. The overall pump efficiency is 86%.

Oil:
The selected oil has $v = 4.0 \times 10^{-5}$ m²/s at normal working conditions. Density is 858.2 kg/m³

Performance:
The ram is required to move a load of 60 kN on the outward stroke only,

at a speed of $0.12 \pm 10\%$ m/s. On the return stroke the speed should not exceed 0.2 m/s.

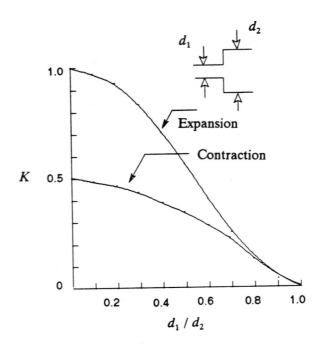

Figure 8.10 Expansion and Contraction Loss Values

Selection of Ram

Referring to Table 8.6, which lists standard off-the-shelf sizes for hydraulic rams, trial and error will show that,

$$\text{Bore} = 101.6 \text{ mm}$$
$$\text{Rod} = 50.8 \text{ mm}$$

will give,

$$\text{Head end area} = 8107.3 \text{ mm}^2$$
$$\text{Rod end area} = 8107.3 - 2026.9 = 6080.3 \text{ mm}^2$$

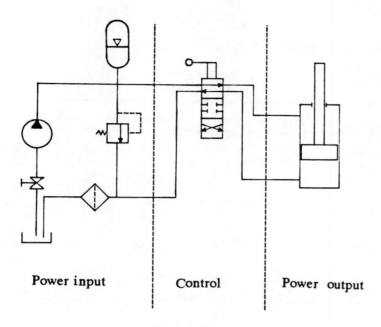

Figure. 8.11 Circuit for Example 8.3

The effective pressure at the head end to move the 60 kN load will be,

$$p_L = \frac{60\ 000}{8107.3 \times 10^{-6}} = 7.4 \text{ MPa}$$

A guess of 15% of this pressure is used to take care of seal friction.

Based on $p_L = 2/3\ p_s$ for optimum power output, the supply pressure should be 12.8 MPa. If we are to keep this cylinder selection, then the pressure losses through the circuit must be confined to,

$$\Delta p = 12.8 - 8.51 = 4.29 \text{ MPa}$$

The speed of the ram on the outward stroke will be,

$$V_{out} = \frac{1.0 \times 10^{-3}}{8.107 \times 10^{-3}} = 0.123 \text{ m/s}$$

and for the return stroke,

Table 8.6

Piston or Rod Dia. (NB)	Size (mm)	Area (mm²)
25	25.4	506.7
35	34.93	958.0
40	38.1	1140.1
45	44.45	1551.8
50	50.8	2026.9
65	63.5	3166.9
75	76.2	4560.4
83	82.55	5352.1
90	88.9	6207.2
100	101.6	8107.3
127	127.0	12667.7

$$V_{in} = 0.123 \times \frac{8107 \times 10^{-3}}{6.080 \times 10^{-3}} = 0.164 \text{ m/s}$$

Pump Suction Line

The next important calculation is to make sure the inlet pipe to the pump does not cause cavitation. According to Table 8.1, the pipe diameter most available for flow rates up to 1.0×10^{-3} m³/s is 32 mm NB, however remember to use ID for calculations.

The Reynolds number for the pipe will be,

$$Re = \frac{K_1 Q}{\nu} = \frac{36 \times 1.0 \times 10^{-3}}{4.0 \times 10^{5}} = 900$$

which is within the laminar range, so the friction factor f will be,

$$f = \frac{64}{Re} = \frac{64}{900} = 0.0711$$

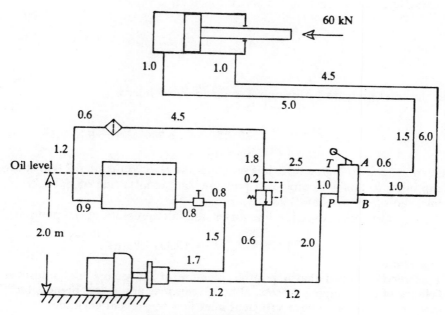

Figure 8.12 Physical Layout

From Figure 8.12, the total length of pipe will be 4.8 m, hence the loss coefficient will be,

$$K_{pipe} = f\,\frac{l}{d} = \frac{0.0711 \times 4.8}{35.1 \times 10^{-3}} = 9.72$$

To this we have to add the loss coefficients for two bends, using Table 8.4,

$$K_{bends} = 2 \times 2.3 = 4.6$$

and a gate valve,

$$K_{gate} = 0.4$$

assuming the same Reynolds number in each case.

These loss coefficients can be added together,

$$K_{total} = 14.72$$

and the total pressure loss from reservoir to pump inlet is,

$$\Delta p = \frac{14.72 \times (1 \times 10^{-3})^2}{2.181 \times 10^{-9}} = 6.749 \times 10^3 \text{ Pa}$$

Referring again to Figure 8.12, it is seen that the reservoir is sited 2.0 m above the pump inlet, so this will provide a pressure on the inlet side of 17.08 kPa, since 1 cm head of oil = 0.0854 kPa.

Taking into account suction line losses, the inlet pressure at the pump will be,

$$17.08 - 6.749 = 10.331 \text{ kPa(g)}$$

above atmosphere.

It is recommended that a positive pressure at the pump inlet improves the efficiency of the pumping process, although this may not always be possible. The important feature is to have sufficient inlet flow to prevent cavitation.

Pressure Losses for the Outward Stroke

According to Figure 8.12, the delivery line from the pump to the ram is 13.5 m long. Referring to Table 8.1, a suitable pipe size would be 20 mm (NB),

$$Re = \frac{K_1 Q}{\nu} = \frac{61 \times 10^3}{4 \times 10^{-5}} = 1525$$

which is within the laminar range, so the friction and loss factors are,

$$f = \frac{64}{Re} = \frac{64}{1525} = 0.042$$

$$K_{pipe} = f\frac{l}{d} = \frac{0.042 \times 13.5}{20.9 \times 10^{-3}}$$

Alternatively, calculations can be carried out by summing the loss coefficients, rather than calculating the pressure loss at each stage.

There are five right-angled bends, which, referring to Table 8.4, will each contribute a loss factor of 0.75,

$$K_{bend} = 5 \times 0.75 = 3.75$$

There are two junctions, one is the normal type, and the other is the tee into the accumulator,

$$K_{tee} = 2 \times 1.55 = 3.1$$

There is an expansion going from the delivery pipe to the ram, which, referring to Figure 8.10, gives,

$$K_{exp} = 1.0$$

The total loss coefficient between the pump and the ram excluding the valve is,

$$K_{total} = 34.98$$

and the pressure drop will be,

$$\Delta p = \frac{K_{total} \, Q^2}{K_2} = \frac{34.98 \times (1 \times 10^{-3})^2}{2.74 \times 10^{-10}} = 127.7 \text{ kPa}$$

The flow path through the directional control valve is P to A, and for a Reynolds number of 1525, the loss coefficient can be estimated as,

$$K_{valve} = 32$$

so that,

$$\Delta p = \frac{K_{valve} \, Q^2}{K_2} = \frac{32 \times (1 \times 10^{-3})^2}{2.74 \times 10^{-10}} = 116.8 \text{ kPa}$$

Note that the valve contributes nearly as much pressure loss as the rest of this part of the circuit. The total loss from the pump to the ram is,

$$\Delta p = 127.7 + 116.8 = 244.5 \text{ kPa}$$

The return line from the ram to the tank must also be included. Since this is also a delivery line when the directional control valve is reversed, it will have the same diameter, but the flow rate will be different due to the differential area of the ram piston. Using 20mm (NB) pipe again, the line length is 22.0 m, and the flow will be,

$$Q = (1 \times 10^{-3}) \times \frac{6.08 \times 10^{-3}}{8.107 \times 10^{-3}} = 7.49 \times 10^{-4} \text{ m}^3/\text{s}$$

$$Re = \frac{K_1 \, Q}{\nu} = \frac{61 \times 7.49 \times 10^{-4}}{4.0 \times 10^{-5}} = 1143.7$$

$$f = \frac{64}{Re} = \frac{64}{1143.7} = 0.056$$

Now determine the loss coefficients between the ram and the tank,

$$K_{pipe} = f \frac{l}{d} = \frac{0.056 \times 22.2}{20.9 \times 10^{-3}} = 59.48$$

In addition there are five right-angled bends,

$$K_{bend} = 5 \times 0.75 = 3.75$$

one tee,

$$K_{tee} = 1.55$$

an exit contraction from the ram,

$$K_{con} = 0.5$$

an entry expansion to the tank,

$$K_{exp} = 1.0$$

giving a total loss coefficient of,

$$K_{total} = 66.3$$

The direction of flow through the directional control valve is B to T in this case, giving a loss coefficient of,

$$K_{valve} = 48$$

in addition there is a filter,

$$K_{filter} = 4$$

This results in a total loss coefficient of,

$$K_{total} = 118.3$$

and a pressure drop of,

$$\Delta p = \frac{184.6 \times (7.49 \times 10^{-4})^2}{2.74 \times 10^{-10}} = 377.9 \text{ kPa}$$

The total pressure drop from the pump to the tank for ram extension is,

$$\Delta p_{total} = 244.5 + 377.9 = 622.4 \text{ kPa}$$

This is well below the 4290 kPa available to develop the flow rate and look after the pressure losses in the circuit. It is also advisable to check the losses for the return stroke.

Input Power to the Pump

The next calculation is to determine the power requirement for the electric motor used to drive the pump. In the previous section it was estimated that 622.4 kPa pressure would be used up in losses. The losses around the circuit can then be expressed in terms of efficiencies.

The circuit efficiency is taken as the ratio of power output to power input. Hence, based on the calculated losses and flows,

$$\text{Delivery line} = 2.445 \times 10^5 \times 1 \times 10^{-3} = 244.5 \text{ W}$$

$$\text{Return line} = 3.779 \times 10^5 \times 0.7491 \times 10^{-3} = 283.0 \text{ W}$$

The output power W_o developed by the ram is,

$$W_o = 1.15 \times 60\,000 \times 0.1234 = 8515 \text{ W}$$

Thus the power the pump must supply will be,

$$W_p = W_o + W_{loss} = 8515 + 244.5 + 283 = 9042.5 \text{ W}$$

If the over efficiency of the gear pump is 86%, then the power supplied to the pump has to be,

$$W_i = \frac{9042.5}{0.86} = 10514.5 \text{ W}$$

Hence a 10.5 kW electric motor is required, or the nearest standard size. The circuit efficiency is therefore,

$$\frac{W_o}{W_i} = \frac{8515}{10\,514.5} \times 100 = 80.98\%$$

8.5 Heat control in hydraulic circuits

Since hydraulic systems generate heat, they must operate above ambient temperature to allow dissipation of this energy to the surrounding environment, otherwise it must be transferred to the coolant of a heat exchanger.

At the other end of the scale, the highest recommended temperature for industrial hydraulic oil is 48.8°C, and a general working temperature should be around 46.1°C. High temperatures cause oil degradation, resulting in wear. There are some super-systems with special seals and fluids that operate up to 260°C.

Heat is a form of energy, and the amount of heat is usually signified by Q, while heat flow is signified by q,

$$q = \frac{dQ}{dt} \tag{8.19}$$

where Q is measured in Joules, and q is in J/s.

Thermal and mechanical energy can be interchanged, so that,

Joule (Thermal) = 1 Nm (Mechanical)

The two basic variables associated with thermodynamics are heat flow (flux) and temperature. These are the effective flow and effort variables that are used for analogies, and would correspond to current and voltage, liquid flow and pressure, velocity and force. However, there is a small difference in that for electrical, fluid and mechanical problem, the product of effort × flow is power; this is not the case in thermodynamics, since the flow variable (heat flow) is already power.

The specific heat of any substance is defined as the amount of heat required to raise the unit weight of that substance by 1° of temperature. For gases there are two ways of measuring specific heat,

$$C_p \text{ at constant pressure}$$
$$C_v \text{ at constant volume}$$

In liquids and solids, there is very little difference in value between C_p and C_v. So if C_p is the specific heat of a substance at constant pressure, then by definition,

$$C_p = \frac{dQ}{dT} \qquad \text{for unit mass}$$

or,

$$mCp = \frac{dQ}{dT} \qquad \text{for mass } m \qquad\qquad (8.20)$$

$$\int dQ = \int mCp \; dT$$

or,

$$Q = mCp \int_{T_1}^{T_2} dT$$

This is the quantity of heat Q needed to raise the temperature of mass m from T_1 to T_2. The mass now stores this heat energy, and therefore acts as a thermal capacitance.

Another way of looking at this is to write,

$$Q = mCp \int_{T_1}^{T_2} = mCp \; (T_2 - T_1) \qquad\qquad (8.21)$$

but heat flow is,

$$\frac{dQ}{dt} = q$$

and therefore,

$$q = \frac{dQ}{dt} = mCp \frac{d\,(T_2 - T_1)}{dt} \tag{8.22}$$

So if $q \equiv$ current (i) and $(T_2 - T_1) \equiv$ Voltage drop (V) then by comparison with equation (8.20),

$$i = mC_p \frac{dV}{dt}$$

$$= C \frac{dV}{dt}$$

so that electrical capacitance (C) is analogous to the thermal capacitance (mC_p).

EXAMPLE 8.4

A hydraulic pump, delivering 0.63×10^{-3} m³/s at 20.67 MPa, would produce,

$$\text{Output power} = 0.000\,63 \times 2.067 \times 10^7 = 130\,22.1 \text{ W}$$

If the pump's overall efficiency is 85%, then the input power must be,

$$\text{Input Power} = \frac{13\,022.1}{0.85} = 15\,320.1 \text{ W}$$

Hence,

$$(15\,320.1 - 13\,022.1) = 2298 \text{ W or J/s}$$

is converted into heat. If there is no means of taking the heat away from a hydraulic circuit, say by heat transfer, then it will be stored in the mass of the hydraulic pump, causing the temperature to rise. Increasing the pump efficiency would of course improve the situation.

In designing any hydraulic system, it is important that a heat balance is achieved at an acceptable working temperature. Heat can be generated in a fluid power circuit from:

1. Orifices in all types of valves used to control flow pressure. The flow condition is mainly turbulent and can even have local cavitation. This area is the main source of heat generation.

2. Pressure drop due to resistive characteristics also occurs in hydraulic lines, fittings, filters and internal passage ways of components. Collections of contamination will increase the problem, since flow resistance is increased.

3. Leakage flow losses in pumps, motors and valves.

4. Seal friction.

5. Compression of the oil, especially where there is entrained air at high pressure. Rapid cycling of gas-charged accumulators will cause an increase in temperature in circuits.

Heat energy going into a system must be accounted for either as temperature rise or transfer of heat out of the system. Heat in fluid power circuits can be transferred from or through the circuit by:

(a) Conduction
This is a dissipative process and therefore can be called a thermal resistance element,

$$q = \frac{\sigma A}{l} (T_2 - T_1) \text{ W} \qquad (8.23)$$

where

$$
\begin{aligned}
q &= \text{heat flow (W)} \\
T_2 - T_1 &= \text{temperature drop (K or °C)} \\
\sigma &= \text{thermal conductivity (W/m.K)} \\
A &= \text{section area (m}^2\text{)} \\
l &= \text{length of a conduction path (m)}
\end{aligned}
$$

An example of this (Figure 8.13) is the passage of hot oil in a pipe, carrying heat energy from one component to another.

(b) Convection
This is another dissipative process involving the passage of heat energy from the system to the outside environment. The relationship is,

$$q = hA\,(T_2 - T_1)\ \text{W} \tag{8.22}$$

where

h = heat transfer coefficient (W/m²·K)

A = surface area (m²)

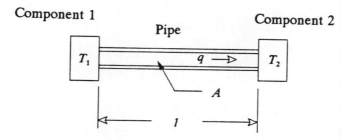

Figure 8.13 Conduction

This is the process of heat generated in the system being passed through the walls of the reservoir and components to the outside air, as shown in Figure 8.14. Here the heat flows through a thin layer of fluid (boundary layer), which adheres to the wall. A true model is more like that shown in Figure 8.15. The heat flow q goes through all three thermal resistances, so that,

$$T_{oil} - T_{air} = q\left(\frac{1}{h_{oil}\,A}\right) + q\left(\frac{l}{\sigma A}\right) + q\left(\frac{1}{h_{air}\,A}\right)$$

$$= \left(\frac{1}{h_{oil}} + \frac{l}{\sigma} + \frac{1}{h_{air}}\right)\frac{q}{A} \tag{8.25}$$

In addition to dissipation, energy can also be stored. However, while there is no such property as thermal inertia, but there is thermal capacitance,

$$q = C_T \frac{d}{dt}(T_2 - T_1) \qquad (8.26)$$

where

C_T = thermal capacitance = mCp (J/K)
C_p = specific heat (J/kg.K)
T_2 = Temp. of body relative to T_1
T_1 = the reference temperature
m = total mass of elements

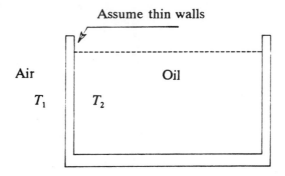

Figure 8.14 Convection

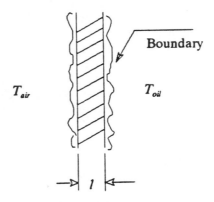

Figure 8.15 Better Wall Model

A complete hydraulic system, such as a pump set, can be considered as a mass of material consisting of pipes, valves, etc., and the working fluid. This mass is surrounded by air at ambient temperature. Inside the mass heat is generated continuously, transferred around the system, and in turn raise the temperature of the mass above ambient. Heat transfer therefore occurs to the surrounding environment.

A specific amount of power is put into the fluid power circuit, and a specific amount of power is taken out of the circuit through a ram or motor to do useful work. The power that is lost is converted into heat,

$$\text{Power input} - \text{Power output} = \text{Power converted to heat}$$

This is the heat input to the system q_1. Part of the heat is dissipated to the environment and part is stored,

$$q_{in} - q_{out} = q_{stored}$$

If we know the system efficiency (η), then q_{in} can be estimated from,

$$q_{in} = Q \times P_s (1 - \eta) \text{ W}$$

where
Q = Flow m^3/s
p_s = Supply pressure Pa
η = Overall system efficiency

The heat output q_{out} is mainly by convection, involving heat transfer,

$$q_{out} = hA (T_2 - T_1)$$

The heat stored in the oil, and metal components is expressed as,

$$q_{stored} = mC_p \frac{d}{dt} (T_2 - T_1) \qquad (8.27)$$

Hence the heat energy balance equation gives,

$$q_{in} - hA(T_2 - T_1) = mC_p \frac{d}{dt} (T_2 - T_1)$$

Let $T = (T_2 - T_1)$, then,

$$\frac{mC_p}{hA} \frac{dT}{dt} + T = \frac{q_{in}}{hA} \qquad (8.28)$$

which describes the time history of temperature rise or fall above ambient due to energy conversion. To determine the time history between ambient and steady state, the solution of this first-order equation is,

$$T = \frac{q_{in}}{hA} \left(1 - exp \left[- \frac{hA}{mC_p} \right] t \right) \qquad (8.29)$$

which says that the temperature reaches 63.2% of its final steady state value in,

$$t = \frac{mC_p}{hA} \text{ s}$$

Typical values are,

$$h = 11.0 \text{ W/m}^2 \text{ K}$$
$$C_p = 2095 \text{ J/kg K}$$

The values for the heat transfer coefficients vary greatly with the condition of the oil storage tank. With poor air circulation and dirty surfaces, h is as low as 8.5, while on the other hand if the air circulation is good and the tank is clean and painted, h can increase to 28. As a comparison, heat exchangers range from 450 to 568 W/m^2 K. Heat generated above 3000 W, usually needs a cooling system of some sort, if the pump is to be run for extended periods. It is unlikely that a large tank would provide sufficient cooling.

In estimating the effectiveness of a storage tank to dissipate heat, it should be noted that if the tank is on or near the floor, its bottom surface area is lost. In addition, the top of the tank is not fully effective, since there is an air space between the oil surface and the top of the tank. Usually you can count on only about 60% of the total surface area being of any use for getting rid of heat.

EXERCISES

8.1. A power transmission system uses 25 m of 20 mm (NB) pipe, with oil of density 870 kg/m^3. The viscosity of the oil is 40 cS. For a flow rate of 0.314 l/s, determine the pressure loss in the pipe. If the flow rate is increased to 2.5 l/s, find the new pressure drop.

8.2. Water is flowing in a 8 mm (NB) pipe of length 3.5 m. What is the largest allowable pressure drop that can be applied across the pipe and still maintain laminar flow conditions?

8.3. A system consists of a pipe of length 15.25 m and diameter of 10 mm (NB). At the working temperature, the oil has a kinematic viscosity of 4×10^{-5} m²/s and a density of 875 kg/m³. Determine the maximum power available when the upstream pressure is 7 MPa and laminar flow is maintained in the pipe.

8.4. The pump set layout shown in Figure 8.16 is required to deliver a flow rate of 2.0 l/s at 10 MPa, to a system represented by a fixed orifice. The following information is provided:

The suction line *AB* is 1.2 m long with one 90° bend in it.

The delivery line *CD* is 12 m long.

The return line *EF* is 12.5 m long with three 90° bends in it.

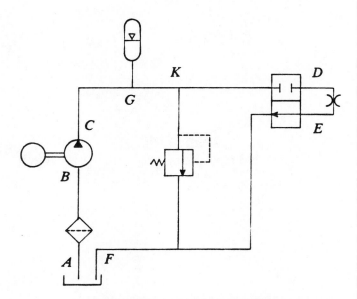

Figure 8.16 Circuit for Example 8.4

The relief valve is teed to the delivery line, as is the accumulator.

The pressure loss through the strainer in the suction line is 13.8 MPa.

The circuit this pump set is supplying can be represented by an orifice with a pressure drop of 5 MPa.
    Determine,

(a) Your choice of pipe diameters.
(b) The suction line pressure drop.
(c) The input power requirement of the pump, if its overall efficiency is 80%.

8.5. A hydraulic circuit, in a manufacturing plant, operates with a oil flow rate of 0.06 m³/min and a supply pressure of 12.5 MPa. If a 600 litre storage tank, of effective surface area equal to 3.0 m², is used to hold the hydraulic oil, how long can the pump operate before the recommended oil temperature is exceeded? Assume the circuit to be 68% efficient and that the ambient temperature is 26°C.

Problems

1. A circuit consists of a pump connected to a hydraulic motor, whose speed is controlled by a simple variable orifice in the delivery line. The system pressure is set at 10.35 MPa. The pump has a displacement of 0.135×10^{-3} m³/rev and a shaft speed of 1740 rpm. The volumetric efficiency is 95%.

The motor has a displacement of 0.18×10^{-3} m³/rev, a volumetric efficiency of 95% and an overall efficiency of 76%. The variable orifice is described by,

$$Q = 3.12 \times 10^{-2} a\sqrt{\Delta p}$$

where the maximum area of the orifice is 18 mm².

The motor controls a torque load of 75 N.m. Determine the maximum flow required through the valve and if there is enough flow available from the pump. Find the speed of the motor, if the valve is 60% open.

2. The upstream pressure at a 1.0 mm diameter orifice is 1.0 MPa, while the air pressure downstream is 0.8 MPa. The upstream temperature is 30°C. The measured mass flow is 1.2×10^{-3} kg/s. Estimate the discharge coefficient.

3. Calculate the power required at the input shaft to a pump, which is moving oil from a tank, if the flow rate is 900 ml/s and the delivery pressure is 22 MPa. The volumetric efficiency is 87% and the pump shaft speed is 1800 rpm. The pump drag coefficient is 0.0018 N.m.min/rev.

4. (a) The pressure drop along a 2.5 m length of 8 mm (NB) pipe is 0.25 MPa. What is the flow rate and the Reynolds number, if the oil viscosity is 50 cSt? Assume laminar flow conditions.

(b) A pipe has a length of 20 m and diameter of 10 mm (NB). At the working temperature of the oil, the kinematic viscosity is 4×10^{-5} m²/s and the specific gravity is 0.875. Determine the maximum output power the fluid can transmit, when the upstream pressure is 8 MPa(g) and laminar flow is maintained in the pipe.

5. A single-ended ram is extending against a constant load of 38 kN. The full area end of the ram is 25 cm², while the piston rod diameter is 3 cm. A flow rate of 425 cm³/s is measured flowing into the ram. Movement of the ram is controlled by an orifice in the return line to the tank. The pressure at the ram outlet port and upstream of the orifice is 6.5 MPa. Determine:

(a) The flow out of the return line.

(b) The pressure at the full area end of the ram.

(c) The orifice diameter.

6. (a) Oil has 2% air by volume entrained in it and the pressure is changed from 10 to 15 MPa. What is the average value of the effective bulk modulus? Assume the unaerated oil has a bulk modulus of 14×10^8 Pa.

b) A cylinder holds 2 l of oil, and the applied pressure is increased from 0.5 to 20.5 MPa. Calculate the volume of oil which must be pumped into the cylinder if:

1. The cylinder is rigid.

2. The cylinder increases in volume by 0.01% for every 0.1 MPa of applied pressure.

Assume the oil bulk modulus to be 13.8×10^8 Pa.

7. In purely mechanical systems, the transfer of the effect of inertia through gear trains involves the square of the gear ratio between shafts. In fluid power circuits, there is an equivalent effect which involves the square of the ratio of the cross-sectional areas. Consider the case of a double-acting, double-ended ram of effective piston area A, pushing oil through a return line of cross sectional area a, to the tank. If M is the mass being moved by the ram and includes the mass of the oil in the ram, and m is the mass of oil in the return line, determine:

(a) An expression for the effective mass that has to be accelerated by the ram.

(b) Given that,

Return line diameter(ID)	015.80 mm
and length	005.00 m
Piston bore	082.55 mm
Piston rod diameter	025.40 mm
Ram stroke	254.00 mm
Mass load	045.30 kg

Calculate the value of the effective mass.

8. A double-acting ram of effective cross-sectional area 645 mm² and ram stroke 150 mm is used to control the velocity of a mass of 25 kg. The motion of the ram is opposed by viscous friction only, so that dry friction can be ignored. The coefficient of viscous friction is given as 2.6 N.s/mm.

   (a) Determine the natural frequency of the system when using industrial hydraulic oil as the fluid.

   (b) Determine the damping ratio.

Repeat the calculation for water as the fluid.

9. A hydraulic circuit consists of a four-way, two-position directional control valve, and a double-acting, double-ended ram. Assume that the steady flow characteristic of the valve is given by,

$$\Delta p = \frac{Q^2}{K}$$

A mass of 2500 kg is to be moved by the ram on a horizontal plane, under the control of the valve. The effective piston area is 3×10^3 mm². Opposing the motion, and in addition to the mass, is a constant force of 500 N and a viscous friction of 3.0 N.s/m.
   A flow test carried out on the valve shows that for a flow of 500 ml/s, the pressure drop is 2.5 MPa. The supply pressure is given as 10 MPa.
   Determine the acceleration of the load at optimum power output from the ram.

10. A double-acting hydraulic ram is controlled by a four-way valve. The ram stroke is 150 mm and the effective piston area is 645 mm². This arrangement is

used to control the velocity of a mass of 25 kg. The viscous friction coefficient is 2.6 x 10^3 N.s/m. If the pressure gain characteristic of the valve is 9600 mm^5/N.s, estimate the damping ratio for the system.

11. A valve with annular control orifices is used to control a loaded ram. The supply pressure is given as 20 MPa. If the maximum spool travel is 0.6 mm and the spool diameter is 0.5 mm, find:

   (a) The approximate expressions for the valve flow and pressure gains.

   (b) The magnitude of the flow when the system operates at optimum power transfer conditions with a valve displacement of 0.3 mm.

12. A four-way valve is used to control the flow to a ram, which has an effective area of 31.6 mm^2. The ram is used to move a mass of 40 kg and there is a spring of stiffness 375 N/mm between the mass and the piston rod. The total volume of oil trapped in the ram is 8.19 x 10^3 mm^3. The bulk modulus is 1240 N/mm^2. The valve has a flow gain of 64.5 x 10^5 and a pressure gain of 710 mm^5/N.s. Both these values were determined at a steady–state position with the pressures each side of the piston equal to half the supply pressure. Determine:

   (a) The relationship between the valve input and the position of the mass.

   (b) The value of the valve modulus.

   (c) The value of the system damping ratio.

13. A hydraulic circuit consists of a four-way control valve and a cylinder with a bore diameter of 8.255 cm. The rod diameter is 5.08 cm. Each of the two sets of circular valve metering ports controlling the flow in and out of the ram has an area of 1.27 mm^2/mm of valve movement. If the oil pressure is 10.34 MPa, determine:

   (a) The pressure drop per control port for maximum power transmission.

   (b) The oil flow through the valve in m^3/s under these conditions, if the valve displacement is 2.54 mm, given that the discharge coefficient is 0.61.

   (c) The piston speed and available output force under these conditions.

   (d) If the stroke of the ram is 15.24 cm and a mass of 28 kg is attached to the rod, calculate the expected natural frequency.

Assume an oil density of 858 kg/m³, and a bulk modulus of 1400 N/mm².

14. Two double-acting rams operate in sequence. The first ram extends in 5 s and requires 5 x 10⁻² m³ of oil to complete its stroke. There is a pause of 4 s, the second ram extends in 10 s and requires 2.5 x 10⁻² m³ of oil to complete its stroke. There is a 3 s pause after which both rams retract in 3 s. Before the cycle is repeated, a dwell period of 135 s occurs. The maximum hydraulic pressure is fixed at 20 MPa, the minimum pressure for the two rams during extension is 11.7 MPa, and the minimum pressure during retraction is 7.5 MPa.

Determine the size of a suitable accumulator for the system, if the precharge pressure is 6.5 MPa. Compare the pump power requirements with and with out the accumulator.

15. A variable capacity pump is used to power a fixed capacity motor. The details of the two units are given as:

(a) Pump

Maximum Displacement	16.4 x 10⁻⁵ m³/rev
Shaft Speed	1500 rpm
Mechanical Efficiency	85%

(b) Motor

Displacement	6.5 x 10⁻⁵ m³/rev
Mechanical Efficiency	85%
Inertia Load	1.0 kg.m²

The slip flow coefficients for both units is 0.9 x 10⁻⁵ m³/s per MPa. Ignoring the effects of compressibility and pipe losses, determine:

(a) The acceleration of the hydraulic motor when its speed is 1980 rpm and the pump displacement is at 60%.

(b) The power output required from the electric motor driving the pump.

Assuming the friction to be very small:

(c) The time taken for the load to reach 98% of its maximum speed when the pump displacement is subjected to a step change from 0 to 50% of its maximum value.

Answers

Chapter 1

1.1. 37.8°C. 1.2. 1.754 MPa. 1.3. 129.22 s. 1.4. 864 strokes, 0.17 W.
1.5. 8.38 m³/min. 1.6. 9.93 x 10⁻³ m³/min. 1.7. 6.26 kg, 0.59 MPa(a).

Chapter 2

2.1. $\dfrac{Y}{Q_1} = \dfrac{(RA\ /k)}{[1 + (RA\ ^2/k)\,s]}$, Simple lag.

2.2. $\dfrac{y}{x} = \dfrac{80\,(1 + 4s)}{[s\,(s + 2)(s + 3) + 32s](1 + 4s)\ +\ 160}$, 0.5.

2.3. $\dfrac{h_1}{Q_3} = \dfrac{R_1}{(1 + T_1 s)(1 + T_2 s)}$, $T_1 = R_1 C_1$, $T_2 = R_2 C_2$.

2.4. $x = 1 - 1.24\,e^{-0.116t}\sin 0.093\,t - e^{-0.116t}\cos 0.093\,t$.

2.5. 0.325, Plot $\dfrac{\theta_o}{\theta_s}(\omega j) = \dfrac{19.286}{(-\omega^2 + 2.857\,\omega j\,)}$.

Chapter 3

3.1. $\dfrac{\Delta F}{\Delta y} = \dfrac{\gamma\,p\,A^2}{V}$, 0.8 x 10⁻³ m³, 0.0059 m².

3.2. 1.22 x 10⁹ Pa, 1.23 x 10⁹ Pa. 3.3. 35.12 Hz. 3.4. 0.286 m.

Chapter 4

4.1. 0.0576 m.   4.2. 8.5 x 10^{-6} m^3/s.   4.3. 1.308 x 10^{-7} m^3/s.
4.4. 15 x 10^{-6} m.   4.5. 6.09 MPa.   4.6. 4.823 mm.

Chapter 5

5.1. 3.74 mm.   5.2. 1.148 MPa, 1.2 x 10^{-4} m^3/s, 0.0262 m/s, 17 959.9 N.
5.3. Δp_A = 1.125 MPa, Δp_B = 3.126 MPa, 0.103 m/s.   5.4. 0.096 m/s,
7.79 m/s^2.   5.5. 19.1 MPa, 3.18 x 10^3 MPa.s/m^3 (secant), 9.9 MPa,
9.94 ms.   5.6. 6.7 x 10^{-4} m^2, 2.97 mm, 0.89 mm.

Chapter 6

6.1. 776.9 rpm, 12 373.5 W, 168 N.m, 9.443 x 10^{-10} m^3/s/Pa (pump),
9.286 x 10^{-10} m^3/s/Pa (motor), 29.4%.   6.2. 0.77 x 10^{-4} m^3/rev, 75.83 N.m.
6.3. 12.6 MPa, 32.66 l/min, 8.04 kW.   6.4. 0.0116 m/s, 46.1 MPa, 17.33 kW, 86.5%.
6.5. 1.52 x 10^{-5} m^3.rad, 8.838 x 10^{-4} m^3/s, 5.7 kW.   6.6. 70 N.m, 57.4 N.m, 10.5 kW,
8.64 kW.

Chapter 7

7.1. 1.146 x 10^{-3} m^3, 4.0 x 10^{-3} m^3/s.   7.2. 15.6 kW, 48 kW.   7.3. 0.37°C,
31 104 N.m.   7.4. 2.8 x 10^{-3} m^3/s, 43.12 kW, 0.078 m^3.   7.5. 0.035 m^3.
7.6. 188 rev, 7.82 MPa, 38 652.9 N.m.   7.7. 3.52 x 10^6 kg/m^4, 1.75 x 10^5 Pa,
Inductive dominates, 2.11 x 10^{-6} m^3/rad, 170 W, 184.9 W, 0.98 N.m.

Chapter 8

8.1. 583.6 kPa, 1.14 MPa.   8.2. 647 Pa.   8.3. 4945.5 W.   8.4. 40 mm (NB), 25 mm
(NB), 16.8 kPa, 25.8 kW.   8.5. 1.49 h.

Problems

1. 0.89 x 10^{-3} m^3/s, 283.1 rpm.   2. 0.8.   3. 26.16 kW. 4. 0.041 x 10^{-2} m^{-3}/s, 1135.4,
5559.8 W.   5. 304.895 cm^3/s, 22.14 MPa, 2.206 mm.   6. 0.028 x 10^{-3} m^3,
0.068 x 10^{-3} m^3.   7. $M + mA^2/a^2$, 559.9 kg.   8. 155.16 Hz, 195.01 Hz, 0.053 , 0.042.
9. 7.79 m/s^2.   10. 0.195.

11. $\dfrac{\pi c_d d}{\sqrt{\rho}}\sqrt{p_s}$, $\dfrac{\pi c_d d x_v}{2\sqrt{\rho p_s}}$, 0.311 x 10^{-3} m^3/s.

12. $\dfrac{\Delta y}{\Delta x} = \dfrac{2040}{s\,(1.73 \times 10^{-4}s^{2} + 0.0142\,s + 1)}$, 9.08 x 10^{10} Pa/m, 0.541

13. 1.72 MPa, 124.35 x 10^{-6} m³/s, 19 922.26 N, 332 Hz.

14. 0.2589 m³, 18.8 kW, 292.5 kW.

15. 156 rad/s², 51.4 kW, 0.792 s.

References

1. Rouse, H. and Ince, S. *History of Hydraulics*. Dover Publications Inc., 1957.

2. Esposito, A. *Fluid Power With Applications*. Prentice Hall Inc., 1980.

3. Reynolds, O. An Experimental Investigation of the Circumstances which Determine whether the Motion of Water shall be Direct or Sinuous and of the Law of Resistance in Parallel Channels. *Phil. Trans, Royal Society,* Vol. 174, 1883.

4. Martin, H.R. *Introduction to Feedback Systems*. McGraw-Hill, 1968.

5. Rendel, D. and Allan, G.R. Air in Hydraulic Transmission Systems. *Aircraft Engineering*. Vol. 23, p. 337, 1956.

6. Hayward, A.T.J. Aeration in Hydraulic Systems, *Conf. on Oil Hydraulics. Inst. Mech Engr*, London, pp. 216–224, 1961.

7. Martin, H.R. Effects of Pipes and Hoses on Hydraulic Circuit Noise and Performance. *37th Nat. Fluid Power Conf.*, Chicago, Vol. 35, pp. 71–76, 1981.

8. Denny, D.F. Leakage Characteristics of Rubber Seals fitted to Reciprocating Shafts. *Conf. on Oil Hydraulics, Inst. Mech. Engrs,* London, pp. 259–268, 1961.

9. Denny, D.F. Cleanliness in Hydraulic Systems. *Conf. on Oil Hydraulics, Inst. Mech. Engrs,* London, pp 225-235, 1961.

10. Bensch, Fitch, and Tessman. *Contamination Control for Fluid Power*. HIAC Instruments, 4719 W. Brook St, Montclair, CA 91863.

11. Arndt, B. Too Many Rating Systems Confuse Filtration Needs, *Machine Design,* March 12, 1992.

12. McCloy, D. and Martin, H.R. *Control of Fluid Power Analysis and Design.* 2nd Edition, Ellis Horwood, Chichester, 1980.

13. Keating, T. and Martin, H.R. Mathematical Models for the Design of Hydraulic Actuators. *Trans. Instrument Soc. America,* 12, 1973.

14. Lee, S.Y. and Blackburn, J.F. Steady State Axial Forces on Control Valve Pistons. *Trans. ASME,* 74, p. 1004, 1952.

15. Wilson, W.E. *Positive Displacement Pumps and Fluid Motors.* Pitman Publications, 1950.

16. Cross, H. Analysis of Flow in Networks of Conduits or Conductors. *Bulletin of Illinos University Eng. Expt. Station,* No. 286, 1936.

17. Streeter, V.L. *Handbook of Fluid Dynamics.* McGraw-Hill, 1961.

18. Hamilton, J.D. Steady-State Flow Characteristics of Fluid Power Components. *Conf. on Oil Hydraulics, Inst. Mech. Engrs,* London, pp. 234–246, 1961.

19. Hamilton, J.D. and McCallum, J. Fluid Power Circuit Design. *Conf. on Oil Hydraulics, Inst. Mech. Engrs,* London, pp. 247–255, 1961.

Index

255